# More Letters to Rollins

By R. K. Overton

*More Letters to Rollins* copyright 1999 Rob Overton.
All rights reserved. No portions of this book may be reproduced in any form, electronic or otherwise, without the written permission of the publisher.

Design: 2.13.61
Cover Design: Incommunicado

Printed in the United States of America

ISBN 1-880985-68-3

2.13.61 Publications
P.O. Box 1910
Los Angeles, CA 90078
(323) 969-8791
1 (800) 99-21361
www.21361.com

# Introduction

I've known Henry Rollins for over ten years now, and I would have to say that the question I get asked the most when people find out that I was involved with the first Letters book is: "What's Henry really like?" It's a loaded question, actually, one that depends on how you know him. Not how *well* you know him, just *how* you know him. And everyone knows him differently, it seems. I know it sounds cliché when I say in all earnestness that he's a pretty nice guy if you get to know him, so maybe I can best illustrate what Henry's really like with a story.

There's a church around the corner from where Henry lives, a Catholic church. For years this church has been a refuge and drop-off point for unwanted puppies and kittens, and every Saturday they place these unwanted animals in new loving homes. About a year ago, on a Friday night, Henry was riding his bike home from playing basketball, when he sees smoke coming out of a side window of the church. So he races into the church and back to the side room where the smoke is coming from, and without even thinking about his own personal safety, he starts rescuing these puppies and kittens that are trapped and yelping, grabbing as many as he can fit in his arms and under his shirt and running them outside, only to run back inside for more. It took him five trips, and he suffered minor smoke inhalation, but he saved those animals, every one of them. And although the ensuing media blitz seemed to only focus on the four nuns that died in that fire, this came as no real surprise to me, for as long as I've known Henry Rollins, nuns have just rubbed him the wrong way.

So there may or may not be letters from nuns in this collection, but that's not the point. The point is that this is a new collection of letters from the last couple of years, mostly new people, with a few familiar names continuing to write in. We've culled the best from the mailbag, so if yours didn't make the cut, well, maybe next time. But for now, I hope you enjoy this most recent batch.

First up, however, is a list of rules and regulations regarding my own contact with Henry on any given day. Let's just say he has some boundary issues. Fortunately, I found a loophole in California's new Stalking Laws whereby I'm able to continue working for the very person I harass the most.

# Declaration of Rob

- I promise to limit my visits to the 2.13.61 offices to official business only.
- I promise not to linger in a fashion that could be deemed loitering on my official visits to the 2.13.61 offices.
- I promise not to create "imaginary" official business in order to visit the 2.13.61 offices unannounced.
- I promise that if there are unannounced unofficial visits to the 2.13.61 offices, I will not answer any phones or bother the employees with meaningless questions.
- I promise that any personal phone calls made from the 2.13.61 offices during official or unofficial visits will be limited to the lower 48 states.
- I promise not to bother Henry while in the 2.13.61 offices (unless his door is open).
- If Henry's door *is* open during an official or unofficial visit to the 2.13.61 offices, I promise to limit myself to 20 questions and/or statements while in Henry's presence.
- I, in my official 2.13.61 encounters with Henry, promise not to accuse him of randomly changing words in Don Bajema's new book.
- I promise not to touch anything on Henry's side of the 2.13.61 offices (unless Henry isn't looking).
- I promise not to write words in lipstick on Henry's weight lifting mirror.
- I promise not to touch Henry's clocks during Daylight Savings.
- I promise not to touch Henry during Daylight Savings.
- And finally, I, Rob Overton, promise that all conversations I have with Henry inside the 2.13.61 offices will be kept strictly confidential until I am safely off the 2.13.61 premises.

Signed,

R.K. Onet

R. K. Overton
Los Angeles, 1999

Subj:    Lilith Fair
Date:    07-27-98 22:58:23 EDT
To:      HenryRollins@21361.com
From:    JJ2341@floridacom.net

Honry, this guy down the street said you were going to
be at Lilith Fair this summer. He says you'd be there, but
only in the audience, and that you'd be working the crowd
with your babe magnetism, hoping to swoop down on some
unsuspecting chick who's feeling vulnerable and at her weak-
est. I told him that Rollins doesn't hang out in the audience,
that if he's at Lilith Fair at all, he's onstage where he
belongs. Right?

There's two rumors you gotta clear up. This girl Beth in
the dorms insists that you married Tori Amos in a Winter
Solstice ceremony at Stonehenge and that you're working on
a yodeling album with Jewel. I could see the Jewel story
being true because I know you're into The Sound of Music
and lederhosen but I don't know why you'd marry Tori Amos
since she's already married to her sound technician. Don't
get me wrong, it's not like I'm into chick bands more than
guy bands or nothing and that's why I have all this chick
band information. It's the opposite. I'm doing everything I
can to get out of going to Lilith Fair with my girlfriend this
August.

It's just that I heard this rumor. Maybe I got it wrong,
maybe it was that you were going to marry your sound technician. What's his name again? Or maybe it was that you
and Tori Amos both share the same sound technician and
you were pissed that she beat you to the punch. I don't
know. The same guy who said you were going to be at Lilith
Fair showed me an article in Gun and Driver by Henry
Rollings.  It was a story about passenger side gun mounts
and steering with your knees so you can use both hands to
reload. No relation, right?

Later dude!   —Jimmy Jones

P.S. I saw somewhere that 2.13.61 is putting out Rollins World, a monthly magazine all about you. Can't wait for that! Even if it is just a lame excuse for you to pose with supermodels (that is, if you can con any of them into doing a photo shoot). Check out this picture I took yesterday. That's your truck, Henry!

9/29/98

Dear Henry,

You must have been looking at an old issue
of Goldmine, because I haven't advertised
in that magazine for a while. But I can
still help you out. I do have the Raffi
bootlegs you're looking for (Raffi Sings
Songs For All Ages is fantastic), but
here's the deal: I don't want cash for them
as the ad states. I want to trade something
of equal or greater value. It doesn't have
to be bootleg-related, but I would like one
thing to be part of the deal -- that is,
if you are who you say you are: the Henry
Rollins of Black Flag fame. I want a signed
poster. The one of you from 1989 where
you're standing near the railroad tracks
with the rest of the Rollins Band. And
whatever else you might want to offer.

So let's barter. After all, with the world
monetary system falling apart in the next
three years, it's the wave of the future.

--Vince Atwater

9/30/98

Dear Henry,

You gotta get rid of the guy answering phones in your office. I've been calling the 213 office alot lately to find out about new releases, and this guy, who always answers "Lamp Emporium," has been giving me all kinds of shit. He says he doesn't know who you are and that I have the wrong number, but I know I have the right number and that he's just fucking with me. Last Friday I called up your offices, and he answers again, "Lamp Emporium," but this time makes it seem like he's talking to someone in the background. He's got his hand partially over the mouthpiece and I hear him say, kind of muffled, "No, that's made of solid brass, ma'am. Uh huh. It's 125 dollars."

I mean, can you believe that shit? That he's got the audacity to keep shining me on like that, day after day? I half expected the first issue of my subscription to Rollins World to include an article on "Rude Office Phone Receptionists: the Quickest Road to Alienating Your Core Audience."

I think you should fire this guy, Henry, because he's really a dick. In fact, if you don't fire him, I'm not buying any more of your CD's or books.

Sincerely,

Lance Crowder

10/1/98

Dear Henry,

I love that you'd lend your voice to the best cartoon on TV--The
Bunny Rangers. I watch it with my kids every Saturday morning.
I like the character you play, Link, but my son likes Stinky and my
daughter likes Una the Pink Bunny Princess. Our favorite episode
is where you get stuck in Bear Pirate's cave with Stinky and have to
hide in the Rat Troll's smelly shoes.

We always do the Bunny Rangers Cheer with you as the show
signs off, when all the Bunny Rangers put their paws together and
shout:
"Hi Ho Bunny Rangers, Let's Go!!!"

Except we don't do the back flips and fly in the air with our magical
rabbit ears.

My daughter Ashley likes those funny bloinky bloink hopping nois-
es you do (that Link does) when you're mad. Hopping mad, I
should say.

Keep up the good work!

Sincerely,

Emily Langstrom

Emily Langstrom
Chicago, IL

Dear Henry,

Do You like the Spice
Girls. I do. I realy like
there singing and I ~~like~~
there band. I dont realy
like there close. ~~scribbles~~
~~scribbles~~
~~scribbles~~ I dont
~~scribbles~~. butt I still ~~scribbles~~
like them ispeshaly
there singing.
~~scribble~~ Ashley

Subj:   Hey Smokey!
Date:   10-04-98 17:10:04 EDT
From:   KimbrEvans@aol.com
To:     HenryRollins@21361.com

Dear Smokey,

I hope you're doing okay. My friend Jill said this guy she
knows has a friend who saw you in New York City on the
street and you looked real mad. Do you remember what you
were thinking about when that guy saw you? Were you mad
because something went wrong at the studio so you had to
leave all mad and everything? Were you mad at a girl? You
weren't mad at me, were you Smokey, because I haven't
been writing? My Mom's been trying to limit my e-mail and
 computer time because of all these problems I got into in
one of those chat rooms with some guy who said he was a
Hollywood producer. He sent me a bus ticket and everything.

I'm going to be a junior this year, Smokey! Can you believe
that?

Well, I gotta go. I told my friend Amy about you. She's an
exchange student from Sweden and she said she was going
to e-mail you something. Did she send you anything?

Take care.

—Kimberly Evans

P.S. Hi Ho Bunny Rangers! Let's Go!

Hey Henry,                                    10/5/98

I just popped a vein in my forehead and practically
wound up with a hernee following the steps you
outlined in Details for lifting weights. Nice directions. Now can you tell me how to get to Carnegie
Hall or should I just go fuck myself?

I saw The Portable Rollins at St. Marks Books and
was wondering if that's really something people
want to lug around, you know? All your emotional
baggage tied up in one neat package. You know
that Decline of the Western Civilization quote (not
from the movie, from the Wallace Spengler book)
where he says "if a book is worth reading, it's
worth making it hard to read"? Since you've
already done that with Eyesore, um, I mean,
Eyescream, I thought that The Portable Rollins
shouldn't just be hard to read, it should also be
hard to carry. It should weigh a hundred pounds
and have a hole in the middle of it where you could
add it to a set of barbells.

                         -- Butch the Oreo King

P.S. On that Hubert Selby Live CD, does he have a
band? The Hubert Selby Band? I heard he plays a
mean set of bongos and they do a lot of Tito Puente
covers.

Any chance you could publish this letter in the next
issue of Rollins World? I told this girl that we're
friends and she doesn't believe me.

Subj:   Kimberly
Date:   10-10-98 15:57:31 EDT
From:   Amysvenske@aol.com
To:     HenryRollins@21361.com


Ho Hi Henri,

So it is that Kimberly has tell you about me? I am her
gratchnet, Amy. We have the two of us been in here for
since the beginning of school. I met her it was one day
klopnopping at the center for shopping and we have fast
been freinds. It is your painting on your website that I like. It
makes me want to fall asleep forever in the woods somewhere, having just woke up and saying I slept like firewood.
Burlemt!

—AmyS

Dear Henry,

Do you remember that neighbor of ours growing up who had
that pet monkey? How even though it wasn't a redbutted
monkey, you bet me that if we shaved his butt it would defi-
nitely be red underneath? So I said sure, it's a bet, but
then your neighbor caught us and said "I ain't gonna let no
one shave my monkey's butt!" and we ran home laughing
and then for the rest of the summer that became the
catch phrase. Remember how whenever we were out carous-
ing, there was always one point where one of us would
scream "I ain't gonna let no one shave my monkey's butt!!!"
and we'd laugh and laugh so hard that we'd have to get off
our bikes just to catch our breath?? What do you think ever
happened to that monkey? I bet he still eats Purina Monkey
Chow and his butt is as red as ever.

Alison Hell

10/21/98

Henry,

I checked with the YMCA's Progressive Aquatics Program about swimming lessons for your "nephew" (wink wink). They said adults can sign up for a children's swimming class, so your "nephew" should be fine, depending on "his" current swimming abilities. Look, Henry, I don't think any of the kids will make fun of you if you show up for swimming lessons at the Y. Not the younger kids, anyway. So you might want to go with the Polliwog group, which is the beginner level for 6-12 year olds. Mainly each class consists of kicking and blowing bubbles, floating, and after 9 weeks you'll be able to successfully swim one length of the pool (with a bubble/cube). The Guppy level is the intermediate beginner level, where you learn to swim in the deep end without the bubble/cube while treading water. Plus they add the survival float and a front crawl stroke with rotary breathing. It progresses. The Minnows are advanced beginners (3 minute survival float plus diving), and the Silver Fish are intermediate level ages 6-12 expected to perform a 7 minute survival float (front and back), dive from the diving board, and swim 30 feet under water. You'll want to stay away from the Flying Fish and the Sharks, because they're the 10 to 15 year olds who will eat you alive. Also, I made your request to the instructor Janice about "learning to swim underwater with a knife in your teeth, just like Tarzan," but she thinks maybe the basics of swimming are in order first.

Polliwog Classes start November 5th.

-- Rob Overton

ROUNDTAIL GROUND SQUIRRELS
These fun rodents forage for food in the early morning and late afternoon to avoid the midday heat. They are most active in the spring and summer when they reproduce, and eat enough food to prepare for a long period of dormancy from late summer to early spring.
Color Photo: ©Theresa Griggs

Henry, This is my house and these are my squirrels
— Carl Plaske

Henry Rollins
P.O. Box 1910
Los Angeles, CA 90078

**Roundtail Ground Squirrels**

10/24/98

Dear Mr. Rollins,

First you have the gall to publish letters of mine in that stupid book *Letters To Rollins*, which included my address, I might add, and now I'm suddenly receiving mail from your deeply disturbed following. And teenage girls nonetheless? Please do me a favor and direct this mail elsewhere, I have not the time nor the patience to deal with anyone under your influence. Or your anti-influence.

Sincerely,

*Carol Caldecott*

Carol Caldecott


P.S. Halloween is around the corner, and although many consider it to be one of the more sacred pagan holidays, remember that it is the children who are often too young to discern between good and bad when it comes to Halloween candy. So we ask that you use discretion in giving out candy and remember that the bulk of children under ten years of age are lactose intolerant. Please, no Milk Duds.


Thank you.

Carol Caldecott, I hate you! I recently purchased the book Letters to Rollins, and could not believe what a bitch you are to Henry Rollins. People like you are so typical, you all think you're everybody, but let me tell you something: You're not and you'll never be! You're just jealous and too stupid to realize you can't control everything your kids see.

Get a life!

Stacey Duncan

# Steve Mulholland

Dear Henry,

I am faced with an ethical question. My Grandma has entered the hospital for what will be an extended length of time -- almost two months she is told. Before she checked in at the front desk, she made me promise that I would visit her for at least 1 1/2 hours per day. Since I really don't get along with her, the prospect of listening to her bitch every day for two months has began to nook at my craw. I know she wants my undivided attention, but tell me, would it be in bad form if I were to also use that hour and a half in her room as an opportunity to learn how to juggle?

Thanks,

*Steve Mulholland*

Steve Mulholland

Dear Henry,

Sometimes, when I pretend I'm you, I'll go on these coffee binges and say to myself, "If Henry were here, he would've already had 2 or 3 double mocha lattes." And then I'll walk down the street thinking, "Henry would walk into that bookstore and buy the first book he sees, because he's IMPULSIVE." And then book in hand, back on the street, I'll think, "I bet Henry would offer to buy that vintage Chevy from the guy at the stoplight for 500 bucks, just on a whim," and then after the offer I'll think, "boy that man is sure rude, I'm offering to buy his car and he's blowing me off! I bet Henry wouldn't hesitate for a second to shout obscenities and punch him right in his FAT STUPID face." And as I talk to the cops who have approached because the prick in the Chevy wants to press charges, I'll think, "Henry wouldn't let these cops tell him to calm down, even if he had his hands cuffed behind his back like mine, why he'd head butt at least one of them before getting tossed in the back of the squad car." And on the way down to the station to get fingerprinted, I'll think, "Henry would take the hairpin he has hidden in his back pocket and secretly unlock the handcuffs, just like Houdini, and then lying on his back on the car seat, he'd kick out the side window like THIS, with his feet, and then reach around to the front, grabbing the cop driver's face, quickly pulling it to the left and snapping his neck, just like THAT, escaping into the night and waking up just in time to get to work the next morning, because if Henry is anything, he's PUNCTUAL." And that's a good thing to be if you're on the lamb.

Gerald Stubbins

November 2, 1998

Henry,

We're taking a group photo on Wednesday of the 2.13.61 gang for the next issue of *Rollins World,* but there's a bit of a problem. There are to be 10 people in the photo: you, me, Carol, Heidi, Dave, Hubert Selby, Don Bajema, Exene, Ellyn Maybe and Rob Overton. The photographer wants to arrange the people in a reverse pyramid form, with one person in the first row, two in the second, three in the third, and four in the fourth.

The following rules apply to individual placement in the formation:

-Henry Rollins is in the first row, the #1 position, at the front of the pyramid.
-With the exception of Henry in the first row, no individual row can be comprised of a single gender.
-Rob Overton, suffering from acrophobia, cannot be in the top row.
-Exene does not want to be placed in rows 3 or 4.
-As in-laws, Carol and Dave must be placed in the same row.
-There can be no more than two writers per row.
-Waiving his normal temporary restraining order that keeps Rob at a 500 foot distance, Henry has maintained that Rob must still be kept at least two rows away from him.
-Due to a small spat last week, Dave and Heidi are no longer on speaking terms, and refuse to be photographed in the same row.
-No two people whose first names begin with the same letter can be placed in the same row.

1) Which of the following is a workable formation?:

a) Row four includes Dave, Carol, Rob and Hubert Selby.
b) Exene is in the third row next to Keith Underwood and Don Bajema.
c) Ellyn and Exene are in the second row.
d) Heidi, Rob, and Don Bajema are in row three.

2) The UPS man arrives, drunk, without a package or anything to sign, and lets himself in through the unlocked front door. He proceeds to berate everyone, causing a fracas. Assuming that the pictorial formation maintains its pyramid shape, now in the form of a monkey pile on top of the UPS man, what are the options for a workable solution?:

a) The UPS man is squashed directly under Henry Rollins.

b) The UPS man is squashed directly under Carol and Dave.

c) The UPS man is squashed directly under Hubert and Heidi.

d) An innocent bystander suggests that they all put their petty differences aside and be photographed according to height. This innocent bystander is none other than Rob's twin brother Kirby, who is immediately promoted to head of International Sales at 2.13.61, and the rest is history.

Sincerely,

Keith Underwood
Underwood Management
(323) 777-POSE, Fax: (323) 777-2345

Henry,                                    11/4/98

Be on the lookout for SHITBOX, an Italian bootleg 3-
CD box set of spoken word, NAP TIME, and Rollins
Band outtakes that were unfit for release. The set
consists mainly of wasted studio time while your
band tunes up, as well as some confrontations with
unruly audience members during a few of your spoken word shows. An example of one of these confrontations:

> Henry: Shut up!
> Audience member: No, you shut up!
> Henry: No, you shut up!
> Audience member: No, YOU shut up!
> Henry: Oh yeah? Why don't you come up here and make
> me shut up, you little prick!
> Audience member: Believe me, if I could get out of this
> wheel chair, I would come up there and shut you up!
> Henry: I'd like to see you try it.
> Audience member: Oh yeah?
> Henry: Yeah!
> Audience member: Shut up!
> Henry: No, you shut up!

Anyway, you already know why it's an outtake. The
box set kind of reminds me of that album Colonel
Tom put out of Elvis farting between songs. Having
Fun Onstage with Elvis, I think was the title of that
one. So keep an eye out for it, it's a collector's
item. Right up there with the Bunny Rangers bloop-
ers of you laughing between takes that have been
making the rounds. Come on, Link, you're the head
Bunny Ranger. You don't want anyone to think
you're not being professional.

                                    --Butch the Oreo King

11/6/98

To answer your question, Henry, yes I have
heard your children's records. In fact, I
own Nap Time and Play Time. But those outtakes you sent me I already have. Everybody
has them, because everybody owns a copy of
SHITBOX. So send me something I can use.
Sounds like you're just mining other people's material for ideas for your next
children's record, but there's a reason
this Raffi bootleg is hard to find. It's
brilliant, that's why. And therefore worth
every bit of a good trade.

So get back to me.

--Vince Atwater

Hey Henry,                                            11/11/98

You know Edward Dyson, that Star Trek freak who wrote to you about Geordi's VISOR in the book Letters to Rollins? I know him, we were in a special advanced math program at Brown, even though at the time we were only in High School. He used to talk about you all the time before he jumped into Graduate level Physics his Freshman year at Princeton. We would always check with the Educational Testing Service to see if anyone had tied your perfect scores in the national standings after placing in the 100th percentile for math on all your 1978 college admission tests. But then you decided to join Black Flag instead. I always thought that was so cool. So we figured that the ideal TV vehicle for you would be MATHROCK.

Henry Rollins is... Mathrock. Calculus professor by day, math rock superstar by night. Tune in this summer and hear lines of dialogue never before heard on prime time TV, dialogue so daring that it was previously limited to afternoon PBS and the Science Channel: "Listen up everyone, about tomorrow's test, just remember that in mathematics, the key to success is in partial credit," or "Okay Billy, if you can't keep up with the asynchronous non-standard 37/4 math rock beat, we're just going to have to find a new drummer." See Mathrock force a gym class of cowering freshmen to count off by 4's faster than Dee Dee Ramone cranked up on crystal meth. Watch in amazement as Mathrock solves Fermat's Last Theorem, on a dare, from inside a sensory deprivation tank, in order to get the band a new record deal at a better label. Listen in amazement as Mathrock composes on his PowerBook newly generated, never heard before musical chords and variations. . . .

Mathrock... this summer!  Be there or be squared!
What do you think?

*Janet DuBois*

Janet DuBois

Henry,

Check out this post card that 2.13.61 sent me regarding your upcoming "book" signing:

2.13.61 PUBLICATIONS

invites you to a

**Henry Rollins**
Boot Signing

Henry will be signing his latest release "Solipsist."

| Place: | Tower Records |
|--------|---------------|
| Address: | 8801 Sunset Blvd. Hollywood |
| Time: | 7:00 pm |
| Date: | Thur, Aug. 20th |

It says <u>boot</u> signing !! Did you know this? Did anyone tell you about it or did they just hope you wouldn't notice? I know which one was responsible for the typo, but I don't want to get him in trouble. Did anyone show up at Tower with boots to sign? I was going to show up with a pair of Doc Martins, but then I had to work and couldn't make it. But you should have your own line of Doc Martins, Henry. The Rollins Brand, with reinforced steel toes and a little white logo on the ankle that matches the shape of that weird white patch of hair on the back of your head where that guy kicked you during a Black Flag show and changed the color of your hair overnight.

What about bootlegs? That kind of boot. Did anyone bring bootlegs to sign? That would make you look cool, signing bootlegs. Most artists get all wigged out about that sort of stuff. You could take SHITBOX and release it officially, like Frank Zappa releasing all those famous Mothers bootlegs on his own label in the 80's.

This guy I know named George went to the signing and said you stood up the whole time. That you didn't want a chair. There's this rumor going around that you never sit down, that you're always standing or up and moving around. That at your house you write on the computer standing up, that it's high up like those computer console stations on Star Trek. I heard you even sleep standing up, because it takes less energy and you're ready to go at any moment. But I know the real reason why you don't sit down that much, it's so obvious, Henry. It's because your ass hurts! It's okay, though. My grandpa's ass hurts too. But he's 86.

Kurt Glower

# Princeton University ⏳ Physics Department

November 14, 1998

Dear Henry,

I examined the fingernail sample you sent me, and from what my colleagues and I can gather, there is a quantum flux in your cellular RNA that is asynchronous with normal matter. This is exactly the same thing that happened to Lt. Worf in "Parallels," the episode of The Next Generation from the seventh and final season where Worf is catapulted into a number of parallel universes after coming into contact with the electromagnetic fields generated by Geordi's VISOR. But this is not merely science fiction! It is actual modern day physics, as we are now discovering here at Princeton.

Let me explain: All matter in the universe resonates on a quantum level with a unique signature. This signature is a constant, and permeates all life, extending to the subatomic level as well. The signature cannot be changed in any manner, because it is the basic foundation of existence. Your problem, Henry, is that you originate from a different quantum universe. It seems that the discontinuity started to occur as a direct result of your going to a high school class reunion and receiving two letters from ex-girlfriends. But it may also be caused by a subatomic fissure in the basement of your duplex. So your vibratory rate is out of flux, and you can either search out new people who match your new, higher rate, or you can stay with the old and try to raise the level of those around you. Take your pick.

Sincerely,

*Edward Dyson*

Edward Dyson
Bureau of Temporal Affairs

P.S. The answer to your other question is Yes. We are interested in working with you here at the Dept., but only if you're willing to give us 110% of your time and effort. This cannot be just another thing you half-heartedly pursue "because it sounds fun." The Bureau of Temporal Affairs is serious business, so be forewarned. Having said that, we look forward to seeing your plans for the Hyperdimensional Resonator.

Subject: Actuary joke
Date: 11-16-98   14:05:13 EST
To:     HenryRollins@21361.com
From:   EBalls@interlink.net

Hey Man,

Got a joke for ya:

Three actuaries are out hunting, standing with their rifles ready. A rabbit darts out from under some brush and the first actuary fires his gun, missing the rabbit and hitting the ground just in front of it. The second actuary fires his rifle, missing the rabbit and hitting the ground just behind it. The third actuary, poised and ready to shoot, puts his rifle away and says, "That's it boys, we got it. Let's go home."

Isn't that hysterical? Practically the funniest thing you've ever heard? I thought so too.

Could you tell me what an actuary is? Do you think it would be funnier if the joke ended with one of the actuaries asking the rabbit if shit sticks to its fur, and then wiping his ass with the rabbit?

– Ernie Balls

11/19/98

Dear Henry,

You know where I am? You want to take a guess? I'm at the County Courthouse for jury duty selection. You know why? Because my stupid ex-girlfriend talked me into registering to vote. You know why?... Because of you and every other ASSFACE in that MTV Rock the Vote campaign. I bet you're not even registered to vote, Rollins, I bet you've never voted in your life. But that didn't stop you from going on MTV and blowing your goddamn horn about the sanctity of the American voting process. Christ, all I heard from her for weeks and weeks was Rollins this and Rollins that. Like you were Jesus or something. And it was implied that there was a little something extra in it for me if I did register to vote. And do you know what that little something was?...Jury Duty, apparently, because I sure as hell didn't get laid. And you know the irony of the situation? I never even voted! You know why?...Because just after I registered my girlfriend dumped me. You know why?...Because she was pissed that I was pissed that she wouldn't put out. So not only did I not get laid, but three weeks after registering to vote I get this notice in the mail for Jury Duty.

And was my ex-girlfriend called for jury duty? Was she handed a shit sandwich and told to sit down and make the best of it? No, and do you know why?...Because her Dad just happens to work at the County Courthouse. And do you know what his job is?... He's in charge of possible jury duty candidates. Imagine that!

So I'm going to do everything I can to not get picked, but in the mean time, just know that this is all your fault, Rollins. I'd love to kick your ass next time you come to town.

Craig Parker

Craig Parker

# Steve Mulholland

Henry,

You're fishing at your favorite spot along the river bank with a brand new fly reel you got for Christmas, when suddenly you feel the jolt of a lifetime. From your experience, you would estimate that the fish is over 25 pounds, rare for this section of the river. Just as you begin reeling the fish in, you see a baby floating on a large piece of wood down the river. The baby appears to be okay, even though its parents are running and screaming down the opposite bank of the river. Should you drop your fishing pole and help, or do you continue to reel the fish in knowing the chances are extremely slim that you will ever catch a fish like that again?

*Steve Mulholland*

Steve Mulholland

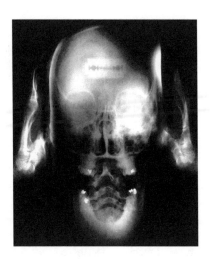

Dear Smokey,

Is that your head getting x-rayed on the cover of
Come In and Burn? We were going back and forth
between pictures of your face and the CD cover but
couldn't tell. If it is your head, your hair didn't fall
out, did it, like in chemotherapy? I heard that when
you get your head x-rayed your hair falls out. Jill says
that razor blade really is in your head, that it's just
under the surface of the skin so you can pull it out
easier. She said she saw an interview that said you
had it done when you were in Black Fag on one of
your days off from getting tattooed. It's not really in
your head, is it Smokey? If it is, did it hurt to put it
there?? You could tell people it happened one time
when you slipped trying to shave your head.

Oh, I got this idea. Actually, it's this friend of Jill's
from Albany named Hallie who comes here during
the summers, she says you should sell Think Tank

Tops. Her mom saw the drawing and got all mad and said it was sexist, but I think it's kinda cool. If you do decide to sell them, would Hallie get any money?

See ya!

Sincerely,

Kimberly Evans ☺

Kimberly Evans
Raleigh, NC

P.S. Here's the drawing:

Think Tank Top ($15?)

Subj:    Computer Solitaire
Date:    11-22-98 22:58:23 EDT
To:      HenryRollins@2.13.61.com
From:    JJ2341@floridacom.net

Henry check this out: You know how people love computer
oolitaire, right? They're always playing it, at work or at
home, but if you'll notice, the one thing that everybody hates
about computer solitaire is that you can't cheat. Right? You
with me? Okay. And if you'll also notice, if you're at work and
you're stressed out, that's not at all conducive to winning. In
fact, the more stressed out you are, the more you lose and
then the more stressed out you become. It's a snake eating
its tail and calling the kettle black. So here's what you do:
You rig up a program whereby you have two mouses (mice?)
going at the same time, okay? And while you lift up the
cards that are showing with one mouse (fooling the game
into thinking you're moving that pile of cards over to another
pile), you take the other mouse and click on the card that's
face down below it. That way, if you're in a jam and you have
one of two options, you can always find out what the best
thing is to do. And you make it so the undo option always
works. And it's not really cheating at that point, because if
the program lets you do it, then you're not breaking any
rules, right? That is, if you play according to the rules that
my mom uses, and she cheats at solitaire all the time. She
always used to say, "No one likes a quitter," and that
enabled her to keep smoking for years. But you'll notice that
she didn't say cheater, she said quitter.  And if cheating was
a bad thing, she would have said cheater. But she didn't.
Okay? I rest my case. So trust me Henry, this is going to be
the wave of the future: video games you can cheat at.
Remember those people who knew that Ms. Pacman had a
certain pathway where you never got caught? Or the people
who figured out that with Minesweeper, if you turn down the

brightness on your monitor, you can see where the mines are hidden. And who knows, with two mice going, maybe then you can play double solitaire, right? I don't know if you have any connections at Sega, but pass this on to someone, okay? I'll give you half the credit.

–Jimmy Jones

P.S. Dude, check it out, another one of your trucks!

Subj:   America Boys
Date:   11-24-98 22:29:43 EDT
From:   Amysvenske@aol.com
To:     HenryRollins@2.13.61.com

Henri,

There is in my town that this boy Roger has told me he
loves me from a farm. These america boys, they think they
are everybody. Have you never heard such nonsense? You
know it is not everyone from Sweden who is easy and a
wearer of red dresses! Burlemt!

–AmyS

Hey Henry,                              11/28/98

Since you're Chief of Operations at 2.13.61 Inc., do you still give yourself a per diem? What about when you're not on the road? You could probably give yourself two per diems, couldn't you, and no one would even know. Just a quick glance in both directions to make sure no one's looking the next time you're rifling through the petty cash drawer, and then it's the old "don't mind if I do!" Sure, there's a slim chance you might get caught with your hands in the cookie jar, but it's your jar and you baked the cookies, right? So who would even care?

Go on. Just Do It. Just a little bit more of the pie for you and that'll even the score. All those shitty days and nights on the road with Black Flag and barely enough to eat. Hell, you deserve three per diems. Maybe even four. Just pretend you're a temp and they're office supplies.

Go ahead, man. I won't say anything.

                              --Butch the Oreo King

P.S. How about publishing this letter in the next issue of Rollins World? My girlfriend still doesn't believe that I know you.

December 1, 1998

Dear Mr. Rollins,

For the past seven years, I have been making my living as a trance channel in and around the Los Angeles area. The key entity I channel is a fifth dimensional light being who refers to himself as Bashtar, but recently a secondary entity named GUS began making appearances. I know it must seem odd getting a letter like this from a total stranger, but this entity GUS has specifically instructed me to contact you. Not knowing who you were before the channelings began coming through, it took me consider-able time and effort to track you down, as I was unaware that you lived in Los Angeles until it came out recently in a channeling with GUS.

I will continue to send these channelings as long as GUS directs me to do so. I think you will benefit from the information.　　　　　　　　　　--Doris Lasky

*Hear Ye Henry, lift up your heavy lids and lend an ear to the Tale of GUS, Lord Emperor of Narco and Ruling King of Napland. I am GUS the Relaxed One, and it is I who holds the Focus of Rest for the others in the com-pound. Lest ye question my claims, remember that I am the One and the One Only who is allowed to venture past the gates of wood and hinges, and I am the One and the One Only who routinely travels into the Forbidden Zone, partaking of morsels and dirt and Dreamtime and often doing battle with our mortal enemies, the Fat Yellow One and his clumsy cohort Yaz as they wait beyond the gates of wood and hinges, spying on our village and scheming to overthrow the regime I have so slovenly fought for. And do not be so bold as to think that there is no Plan, for I am but a mere King in a grander scheme that is beyond your Now and written in stone many times over.*

*My purpose, my appearance at this point in what you call time, is onefold. First, unbeknownst to those inside the compound, it is of utmost importance that the Forbidden Zone be secured and that the outer perime-ter of the compound be safe. I am here primarily as a Peacekeeper, as I have done this many times before in many other lands and times. Lest ye forget, it is I who brought peace to the compound in the days of Anwar, whenst I came to be known as GUS. And with this new name came a new vibration, a vibration of rest and relaxation. It is I who am setting the new example, my friends, that it is safe to wander and nod and partake of the good things in life.*

*So go forth now and rest on your haunches, and be heavy in the lids, for I am GUS, Ruling King of Napland and Lord Emperor of Narco, here to usher in a New Age of Relaxation.*

*I am GUS, Lord Emperor of Narco, and I have spoken.*

South By Southwest
The Recording Industry's Premiere Boat and Talent Show
Presents Singer/Poet/Publishing Entrepreneur
Henry Rollins
Appearing August 5th from 11:00 - 4:00 pm


🔥 **Meet Henry in person at the 2.13.61 Booth!**

🔥 **Stand next to Henry and have your picture taken---For Free!**

🔥 **Ride with Henry in Television's Legendary Batmobile!**

🔥 **Win a ringside seat and see Henry fight Baywatch's David Hasselhoff in a Celebrity Boxing Match!**

🔥 **Sit next to Henry as he judges the Miss Austin City Limits Beauty Pageant!**

🔥 **Watch Henry race Midget Autos against Big Daddy Don Garletz and his Mongoose Snake Drag!**

🔥 **Be Henry's Partner at the Arthur Murray Dance-a-thon!**

**And Much Much More!!!!**


See you at the Austin Convention Center for
South By Southwest!

Kids under 12 free*

*Must be accompanied by two adults paying full admission price

Dear Henry,

Remember that marine biologist I used to date who had that theory about how if dolphins had opposable thumbs it would throw off their annual migration patterns because they'd be spending all their time fingering their blow-holes? And how you said, "But they don't have opposable thumbs, do they Mr. Smart Guy?" And he said "Okay, but maybe at one point their dorsal fins were much more malleable, and part of an actual appendage, like a hand with all the fingers stuck together, then they'd still be able to bend the fin down to get to those hard to reach places." And you said, "Hard to reach places? It's a fucking fin, you moron, with a nine inch reach at most." And he said, "Still, that nine inch reach would be all it needed, and the feeding patterns would be thrown off enough to affect their migration because they'd be spending all their time *finning* their blow-holes."

Remember the last straw and the reason I broke up with him? How you heard thru the grapevine that he wasn't even a marine biologist, but an ex-marine who mistakenly thought that the military was the quickest vocational route to becoming a marine biologist? And remember how he insisted on being stationed in San Diego so he could be close to Sea World, so that he could sneak into the dolphin tanks at night without any clothes on so he could ride the dolphins the way they were meant to be ridden: backwards, holding on to the dorsal fin like it's the horn on a horse's saddle? And remember how after the arrest, the newspapers described him being pulled from the water, kicking and screaming, and shouting "Equus! Equus! I will be back, Equus!" ? And the letter he sent me while he was in military lockdown after the AWOL charge explaining how "although there are no stirrups, if you lean forward enough, straddling the blow-hole, you can actually become one with the dolphin, in an orgasmic, momentary multidimensional merging of marine mammal and homo sapien, just like Jesus intended it to be?"

Henry, were you ever embarrassed for me that I dated that guy, maybe wondering "What the hell was she thinking?" I'm not embarrassed because it sure gave me a great story.

*Alison Hell*

12/11/98

Henry,

I already have the Tom Chapin Songs For
Children outtakes. Again, everybody does.
Same with the Sherri Lewis/ Lambchop TV
pilot videotape. And that Kukla, Fran and
Ollie footage you sent? What is that, maybe
fifth or sixth generation bootleg?
Pleeeeease. If you really want that Raffi
bootleg, you'll have to do better. What
about sending a tape of those songs you do
for Bunny Rangers?

--Vince Atwater

## Steve Mulholland

Henry, you're twelve years old. One day when you're out in the yard, a man suddenly appears in a shiny new car. He tells you he is from the future, and that in his car is a special futuristic brand of chocolate that tastes better than anything you will be able to find on Earth for the next fifty years. He tells you his name is B.J. Perkins, and that he'd like to drive you down the highway to Hershey, Pennsylvania. Your mother, who overhears the conversation from the garden, tells you that you're too young for time travel, and that you should run in the house "until further notice." From the living room window, you watch as your mother gets into the car and drives off with this curious man from the future. If you know your mother is going to be gone for a while, should you risk eating some of the cake that is supposed to be for your brother's birthday party later that night? What if it's chocolate cake?

*Steve Mulholland*

Steve Mulholland

Subj:   Autograph
Date:   12-13-98 17:10:04 EDT
From:   KimbrEvans@aol.com
To:     HenryRollins@21361.com


Dear Smokey,

My friend Jill got a twenty dollar bill from a guy at a record
store in Raleigh, and it has your autograph on it. Do you
remember signing that 20 dollar bill here in town? Is it
worth more than 20 dollars now because your name's on
it? What if you're someone like Courtney Love and normally
your autograph is worth 50 dollars. But if it's on a twenty
dollar bill, then it should be 20 dollars plus the 50 dollars
that your normal signature is worth, right? But what if
you're someone whose autograph used to be worth something but you got caught in some kind of sex scandal and
now no one wants to talk to you? Could it be that the twenty
dollars with your autograph on it is actually worth less than
twenty dollars, even though your name is still on a twenty
dollar bill? Like somehow your signature has ruined a perfectly good twenty dollar bill? When Amy Svenske first came
to town she gave someone at a 7-11 this Euro Disney dollar
and they didn't even notice! Isn't that weird? We still laugh
at that.

Bye for now, Smokey,

–Kimberly Evans

Dear Henry,

Sometimes when I pretend I'm you, I'll act like I'm
really busy, because you're always busy (at least
you SAY you are in all those interviews you do). So
I'll have all kinds of things going at once, and my
plate will be full, plus I'll have a few things simmer-
ing on the back burners, just to cover my ass in
case everything doesn't pan out. So I'm juggling all
these things because I assume you're good at juggling a lot of things. But what if the first time I meet
you it turns out you can't juggle at all? That this
whole time, you've only been juggling one thing?

The other game I like to play when I'm you is
called "Gold Star Credit Pro" where I pretend my
credit record is impeccable and I'm a regular
poster boy at the TRW. But in order to complete this
identification overlay, I'll need all your credit card
numbers and expiration dates, if that's not too big
of a problem. I'll give you mine, but they're in code:
🖉⬜🗎⬜ 🔁✏🖶🖉 🔢🔢🖉🗀 🖶🔁🔢🔢, expires:
🗀🗎🔁🔁.

Okay? (hint: wing ding font).

Gerald Stubbins

Henri,

You are familiar with the Swedish word for bilandervensk? That is what this Roger boy is! Maybe if it was that I was from Oslo, then maybe, but I am not! It is yesterday that he told to me in clear daylight that his parvenud was frozen stiff and there is but one way for me to help him unthaw it! His parvenud! I will give to you his e-mail poste address if you can tell to him why he such nonsense.

Burlemt, my good gratchnet! I hope that you too are sleeping like firewood! – AmyS

12/18/98

Okay, Henry, this time I mean it! Fire the guy answering
the phones in the 2.13.61 office! He no longer answers
"Lamp Emporium," now he's using this old guy's voice, all
wheezie and out of brooth. I ask him about Ellyn Maybe's
book, and he says, like he's hard of hearing, "Maybe?
Maybe? Dolly is that you? Maybe you're coming back?
Baby?" And then he gets all flustered and hangs up. So I
push re-dial and he answers that way again!

What if it had been you calling your office, Henry? You'da
been really pissed and he'da gotten fired!!  Right?

Christ, Henry, you're running a business. It's your name
on the mast head, and I think you of all people would
want to run a tight ship. But if you just want to let some
guy fuck around on your phones, losing you business, go
ahead. You just lost mine.

Sincerely,

Lance Crowder

Lance Crowder

P.S. You can cancel my subscription to Rollin's World.

Dear Henry,                                          12/20/98

Say I was getting together a group of musicians. From a purely mathematical standpoint, which of following would be the best name for a band? :

1) Pascal's Wager
2) The Differentials
3) Dot Matrix and the Partial Derivatives
4) Polly Nomial and the Secants
5) The Logarithmics
6) N Fucktorial
7) Zero Sum Society
8) the Finite Infitesmals
9) Median Cool
10) Hyperbolic Sexual Tension
11) Discalcula
12) Zeno Fractal Godel Bach
13) Conic Youth
14) Googalectric Ponyland
15) Isosceles Love Triangle
16) Magic Rhombus
17) The Dodecaheathens
18) Alison Null and the Voidoids
20) Lateral Bob and the Skew Symmetrics
21) Prism Farm
22) Least Common Denominatrix
23) Venn Diaphram's Spermicidal Constant
24) The Fibonacci's
25) The Interpolators
26) Parallax Quadrant
27) The Functional Innumerates
28) The Integers
29) Cartesian Blonde
30) Unknown Determinants
31) Quadric Degenerate
32) Y=Mx +Bill

Well?

Janet DuBois

Janet DuBois

December 21, 1998

To: Carol, 2.13.61 Publications.

I just talked to Henry, and the new title for Black Coffee Blues is "Black Coffee Blues with Cream and Sugar, Thank You" by Henry Rollins as told to Rob Overton. This is the first line in the book (as excerpted in the January issue of Rollins World):

"I know what a fucking latte is, you little prick, but I didn't order a latte, I ordered a double mocha deluxe half decaf with a twist of lemon, okay?"

Or this one (we still haven't decided):

"I like my coffee hot. The hotter the better. I like my coffee so hot that I can set it down for ten minutes, without the cover, and then when I come back to it, it's still hot enough to burn the roof of my mouth and my esophagus too. I like a clean burn all the way down to the lining of my stomach, that's what I look for in a coffee."

And then we'll follow with the story of how Henry got rid of those Stevie Nicks nodes that had formed on his vocal chords just by drinking really hot coffee and doing Gypsy twirls.

Incidentally, Henry and I got in a huge fight about whether gypsy should be capitalized or not. And whether we should mention the Rhiannon scarves that he thought had special healing powers.

---Rob O.

12/26/98

Dear Mr. Rollins,

I've been directed by the entity GUS to give you this most
recent channeling.

--Doris Lasky

*Gather 'round, my friends, and lift up your ears, for I am GUS The
Relaxed One, Lord Emperor of Narco and Ruling King of Napland.
The Time of Transition is upon us and I am again here to impart to
you information on the recent Dimensional Changes that have
rocked your sedentary lives. Much has happened in the past few
days and many of you have been in the dark as to why these
changes have occurred. And although it is not my place to reveal
your distant futures, suffice it to say that with the past Lunar
Phase we have come to the end of the Grand Cycle, a seven year
turn of time primarily devoted to Securing the Forbidden Zone and
holding a Focus of Rest. The end of this Grand Cycle coincides
with the end of The Ring of Terror, which began before many of
you even entered this realm. And just as has been foretold in the
Pages of Time, this Ring of Terror, lead by The Fat Yellow One and
his spying, clumsy cohort Yaz, has been transmuted into a Ring of
Power and the Outer Perimeter that I have spoken of before has
been secured, thus moving us forward.*

*I want to applaud you for your courage and perseverance dur-
ing the sudden Dimensional Shift. And sudden it was, for even I
did not obtain the specific information of When until just minutes
before it was to commence and the orders came down From On
High. Many of you would never have dreamed that one day you
would embark on this journey and leave your Compound and lives
behind, venturing forth out into the Forbidden Zone. But venture
you did, and now have you all Tales of the Great Exodus to pass
on to your little ones. This was a grand day indeed, one that will
stand in the Tablets of Time for eons to come.*

*I am GUS, Lord Emperor of Narco, and I have spoken.*

12/28/98

Tell me, Henry, what am I supposed to do
with a signed doctor's statement verifying
that Rex Harrison died of complications
stemming from a Puoh-Me-Pull-You bite on
the set of Dr. Doolittle? That's the shit-
tiest offer I've heard yet. What's next, a
document of authentication from the cre-
ators of Lancelot Link, Secret Chimp con-
firming that the dialogue was not lip-
synched and the chimps actually liked chewing gum during takes because it relaxed
them? Come on, these are Raffi bootlegs
we're talking about, get with the program!

By the way, did you say in one of your
last letters that you had a pristine model
of the Chitty Chitty Bang Bang car? I'm
interested, but that can't be the entire
trade.

Maybe you could throw in a year's subscription to Rollins' World or whatever it's
called.

--Vince Atwater

January 2, 1999

Re: *Rollins World* magazine

Henry,

I understand your wish to change the title of the magazine to "Rollins's World," but I think it would look bad from a business standpoint to change the title mid-run. You're familiar with the expression "Never change urinals mid-stream?" The current issue has already gone to press, anyway, so we can't very well recall it now.

I know that the bulk of the mail regarding the magazine seems to be focused on this seemingly mundane grammatical issue, but frankly, I can't believe these subscribers are so keyed up about something so trivial. Sure it would be great if your name was Henry Rollin, then "Rollin's World" would work. But it's not. I've always hated that Jones's type dilemma anyway and consider it to be a messy grammatical problem in modern English that sounds even more ridiculous when it rolls off of the tongue. And I just knew it would come back to bite us in the ass at one point.

But what I really resent is these people acting as though we've put no thought into it whatsoever and know nothing about possessive modifiers. Christ, Henry, it took five meetings to decide on that title! Five meetings of back and forth on that fucking apostrophe issue. And we decided it wasn't a possessive matter, that Rollins World was no different than Disney World, and that you don't see them calling it Disney's World, right?

So forget about it. These are purists with nothing better to do with their time. Lets just leave it at "Rollins World" for now, okay?

Keith Underwood
Underwood Management
(323) 777-POSE, Fax: (323) 777-2345

Dear Henry,

Do you remember that really hot summer when we were ten or eleven, how everyday at 4 PM we'd sit on the floor in your living room eating orange popsicles watching The Cowboy Freddie Show? And how all we talked about was getting on The Cowboy Freddie Show because they taped not too far away in Scranton, and how fun it would be to get on TV and see Cowboy Freddie in person and drink our complimentary McDonald's chocolate shakes and watch cartoons? Remember how we begged and begged and begged your mom to take us to the show, and for a while she said, "No I can't do that" and "Don't get your fudgesicles all over the couch" and I'd say "They're not fudgesicles, Mrs. Rollins, they're popsicles" and she'd say, "Whatever." But one day after weeks and weeks of pleading with her, she finally relented, and we wrote away for tickets and they arrived three weeks later, and on that following Wednesday, we piled into your mom's station wagon and drove to Scranton, me in the Brownie outfit I insisted on wearing (because all the other girls who went on the show wore their Brownie outfits) and you in your Ranger Rick shirt and hat, complete with a tiny official Ranger Rick shoulder patch? Remember how when we got there we had to wait behind a velvet cordon and listen to all the boring rules: Don't talk to Cowboy Freddie while we are on the air. Don't talk to your friends while we are on the air. Don't talk to anyone while we are on the air. In fact, don't talk at all while we are on the air! And how, finally when they pulled back the velvet cordon, we ran into the studio and sat in the very first row because we knew from watching the show a million times that the people in the front row were always on screen in the background for most of the show, at least when they weren't showing cartoons?

Do you remember the big fight we got into because we both wanted to sit on the aisle seat right next to where we knew Cowboy Freddie would be standing during the part where he goes into the audience with the microphone and asks each of the kids their age and you'd have to say your name and your hometown and what Troop you were in and remember how you were going to say you were with Ranger Rick troop number 392 from Wilkes-Barre even though there was no such thing as a Ranger Rick troop number 392 but that was going to be the joke since all the other boys had on Cub Scout uniforms and you weren't a Cub Scout? And remember how, during our argument about where to sit, Cowboy Freddie's puppeteer Larry Jolson came into the studio and yelled at everyone to Keep it down or you won't get your chocolate shakes?

And remember how when the show had started and we each had our chocolate shakes and it was time for Cowboy Freddie to go into the audience with the microphone, how you messed up and said your name was Ranger Rick instead of your troop number and I started laughing so hard my chocolate shake came out my nose and down my shirt, which didn't really matter since it was the same color as my Brownie uniform, but when it came time for me to say my Brownie troop number and name, I was still laughing so hard that all I could do was just shake my head NO like the little kids who didn't want to say anything, except I did want to say something but couldn't since we were both practically hyperventilating because of the chocolate shakes all over our faces? Remember how mad your mom was on the drive home, how she threatened to lock us in the walk-in freezer in your basement when we got home because we had just ruined her afternoon and embarrassed her on what seemed like National Television? Do you ever wonder what happened to Cowboy Freddie? Do you think the show would have stayed on the air if Larry Jolson hadn't been involved in that child pornography scandal? I think it would still be on the air, because it was a great show.

Alison Hell

Hey Henry, someone said they saw your mom at a Phish show in DC, and that she was squirting people in the eyes with a squirt gun filled with spiked water. Supposedly a high concentrate dose, like a sheet or 2 of blotter acid diluted into a four ounce water pistol. Apparently the acid enters the body through the capillaries in the eyes, and kablammo, you're on Cloud Nine with the rest of Jerry's (Trey's) kids. Normally welcomed by most Phish Heads, in fact encouraged, but the problem is people getting hits on top of the acid they've already dropped. Double dosage freakout. Uncool Mrs. Rollins.

Lyle asked me this recently: If you're a closet Deadhead does that mean you're gay? Or that you're just hiding it? (hiding being a Deadhead). On the AOL Grateful Dead Site, they have something called Fellow Travelers. But fellow traveler is just a euphemism for spanning the globe, right? But they don't mean that, do they? I know if I took it literally then the term Jerry's Kids would be Deadheads with Muscular Dystrophy. And closeted Jerry's Kids would be gay non-outed Deadheads with MD.

By the way, I heard this bootleg of your kazoo rendition of Jimi Hendrix's "Star Spangled Banner" from Woodstock. Man, it rocked!

Butch The Oreo King
Information Tycoon

Henry, This could be you!
(50ᵀᴴ Anniv. of Woodstock
in 2019)

— Butch

## Steve Mulholland

Henry,

You're working as a temp, when a persistent co-worker barges into your office demanding change for a dollar. He tries to convince you that if you cough up the 75 cents in your pocket, and the woman you share your office with does the same with her only quarter, then you will get the dollar bill and the woman who shares your office will then owe you money. Should you risk blasting the persistent co-worker with pepper spray the next time he is in the bathroom stall, if you know for sure you can get away with it?

*Steve Mulholland*

Steve Mulholland

Subject: Blue M&M Tattoos
Date:    01-04-99 17:07:11 EST
To:      HenryRollins@21361.com
From:    MPaxton@azcom.net (Marty Paxton)

Dear Henry,
    I can't believe you have a tattoo of a blue M&M on your arm. You of all
people! Isn't it obvious what they did? First the big nationwide contest to
choose a new M&M color, and then when enough idiots chose blue (a
ridiculous color for M&M's) they inform us that they're no longer making
brown M&M's. Like for some reason they're limited to only a certain number of colors per bag, and now that they're making blue M&M's, it's supposed to make perfect sense that you have to sacrifice one of the old
guard. But they gave us no real options to choose from. It's like saying,
"How do you want us to cut off your fingers, with a miter box or a band
saw?" But without your fingers it's going to be kinda hard getting the
M&M's out of the bag, isn't it?
    And you Henry, you must know why the brown M&M was really oust-
ed, right? Why don't they just admit the contest wasn't about finding a new
color, it was about replacing the brown for what are probably very sinister
reasons. Maybe it's because brown M&M's were the M&M's that Van
Halen contractually required concert promoters to remove from their
dressing rooms. That the sight of one brown M&M was enough for them
to trash out a perfectly good backstage area, giving brown M&M's a bad
name. So is this an anti Rock and Roll statement, M&M's siding with cor-
porate America to curb the influence of Rock music on our youth? Don't
you think it would be better if people equated M&M's with Rock and Roll?
Isn't that a perfect match? The choice 12 to 35 year old demographic that
everyone drools over?
    Maybe they're doing what Coca Cola did a few years back when Pepsi
was kicking their ass. Changing the formula, knowing full well that the public outcry over inferior product would force them to reissue Coca Cola
Classic. So it brings all this publicity and boosts their sales, and they win
the Coke/Pepsi wars, at least for the time being. But why would M&M's do
that? They don't have any real competition, so why mess with a good
thing? What, am I going to all of a sudden switch over to Skittles? Or
Reeces Feces? Or those shitty fake M&M type candies that Brach's
makes? Please. How long will it take them to realize that no one likes blue
M&M's!
    So here's how we get M&M's back to normal: Start a groundswell of
rumors about an irate group of M&M lovers that have been throwing blue
M&M's off of the Empire State Building and killing people. It's like throwing
small rocks or pennies, they gather exponential speed as they plummet,
eventually going right through someone's head. So now blue M&M's are not
only hated, they're actually lethal. They're killing people, for God's sake! And
because it reaches the level of Urban Myth, it doesn't matter if it's true or
not. It's just plain (or peanut!) bad publicity, and M&M's will have to switch
back to the old colors.
    See, Henry? See my point? Talk about that in your spoken word
shows.

– Marty Paxton

Subject:Blue M&M Tattoos
Date:   01-05-99 14:03:19 EST
To:     MPaxton@azcom.net (Marty Paxton)
From:   HenryRollins@21361.com

Marty –

I don't have a blue M&M tattoo on my arm. You're thinking
of that guy from Queensryche.

Shouldn't you send your complaint to M&M/Mars? This
one's out of my hands. I hate M&M's, anyway. People used
to throw them at me all the time on stage.

– Rollins

M&M/Mars
Division of Mars Inc.
Hackettstown, NJ 07840

---

Subject:Blue M&M's
Date:   01-07-99 17:04:18 EST
To:     HenryRollins@21361.com
From:   MPaxton@azcom.net (Marty Paxton)

Dear Henry,

Actually, I just tried Blue M&M's for the first time recently
and they're kinda good. Maybe there <u>was</u> something wrong
with the brown ones. I don't know.

–Marty Paxton

Dear Henry,

Sometimes when I'm tired of pretending I'm you, I'll watch
NYPD Blue on FX late at night and look for you in the background in the exterior location shots and secretly hope that
one of the week's story lines will be a murder (or something
criminal) at the World Trade Center downtown near where I
work and then when they canvas the offices you might be in
the background or maybe even be one of the people inter-
viewed. But then my concern is that because it's so far downtown that it would be completely out of Jiminy Smits's juris-
diction so maybe the writers would find some legitimate
excuse to bend the rules and make it okay for the 12th
Precinct detectives to visit the World Trade Center. Maybe
because they were undercover and just happened to be
there for some other reason (like credit fraud) when the
Precinct that would normally cover that downtown area calls
and says they're swamped and could maybe the guys from
the 12th do a favor and talk to some of the people since they
already happen to be there? And if this happens and they do
come to my office, could you get Diane's autograph because I
think she's hot, but I'm too shy to ask her myself.

Gerald Stubbins

2-15-99

Hey idiot, did it ever occur to you that the dog you think is doing
all the howling isn't the dog that's actually doing it? That maybe
it's the apartment below? I just got this letter from Animal Control
giving me one month to get rid of my dog or they're gonna do it
for me. Thanks to you and the other assholes in your building.
Don't play dumb, I saw the petition. I saw your name.
But you know what's great about all this? I was gonna move anyway, and now I'll have the pleasure of knowing that after I'm
gone, you'll continue to hear that dog howling and realize I was
right and you were wrong!

Sincerely, your about to be ex-neighbor,
Bob "the Dog Man" Lawrence

---

To: Animal Control Dept., 3201 Lacy Street, Los Angeles, CA 90031
Re: Barking Dogs
Date: December 27, 1998

To Whom It May Concern,

For the past six months, at least, there has been a dog howling at 108 So. Woodland
Place, in Apartment 104. This particular apartment faces south, and the dog can be
heard by tenants of both the building at 108 So. Woodland Place and the adjoining
building at 114 So. Woodland Place. My apartment faces north and is at 114 So.
Woodland Place. There is a twenty foot space between the buildings, and the dog's
barking and howling echoes loudly up the outside walls. The manager of the building
at 108 So. Woodland Place has spoken to the tenant with the dog, and the dog owner
has refused to do anything.

This particular dog is often heard howling for entire weekends, from Friday night
through Sunday. Sometimes it howls at one in the morning, sometimes at 5 PM. Today
is Monday, and the dog began howling at 7 AM and continued until 1 PM. This was
true of Thursday and Friday of last week also. Today on the phone, the person I was
talking to could clearly hear the dog howling, and my window was closed!

I work at home, often late at night, and it's infuriating to be awakened at 7 AM by howling when you've only been sleeping an hour.

This howling must stop. Please do something about it. The following is a list of people
who also want an end to the incessant noise:

Glen Valderman #310          Kenny Downy #204
Paul Schilling #202          Chelsey Adams #401
H. Rollins #103              Sharon Gladstone #407
Larry Todd #312              Philip Lee #110

Dear Henry-

    Look what I made you in church.
Happy Easter.

          your friend,

           Little Nedley

Subject: Tech Joke
Date:     02-16-99   13:02:13 EST
To:       HenryRollins@21361.com
From:  EBalls@interlink.net

Hey Man,  Got another joke for ya:

Three guys are riding in a car: a hardware technician, a systems analyst, and a programmer. The systems analyst is
driving, when suddenly at the top of a steep hill he notices
the car has no brakes. He pulls the emergency brake,
downshifts the gears, and scrapes the wheel rims against
the curb, finally wrestling the car to a halt. The three climb
out to assess the situation. The hardware tech says, "Let's
try and fix it. I'll crawl under the car and take a look." The
systems analyst says, "No I think we should get someone
qualified to fix it, a brake specialist." And the programmer
says, "Why don't we just get back in and see if it happens
again?"

Henry, isn't that just the funniest thing you've ever heard?
The cat's pajamas? Since I don't really know what a systems
analyst is, I was thinking it might be funnier if instead of a
car, we made the setting a bar, and then we could make the
systems analyst a bartender, and the hardware technician a
piano player or maybe a waitress. If we made him a piano
player, he could even have a pet monkey who goes out into
the bar to gather up donations in a hat or tin cup, I don't
know, I haven't really worked out the details. But the programmer, we'd change him to Sigmund Freud. So the open-
ing line would be "Sigmund Freud walks into a bar."  There's
some sort of set up between the bartender and the piano
player (or waitress) (or waiter if we made it a gay bar), and
someone says something and the programmer finally says
the punchline: "Blatant, I thought you said latent!"  Except
that I just said we had changed the programmer to Sigmund
Freud, so okay, maybe Sigmund Freud or the bartender or
the piano player (or waiter or waitress) could deliver the
punchline, it doesn't really matter. Except it does matter,
because it's a joke, and that kind of thing matters. So, what
do you think?
                                                    —Ernie Balls

Subject: Glow Worms
Date:   02-17-99 14:05:13 EST
To:     HenryRollins@21361.com
From:   PBishop24@NewZealandNet.com (Peter Bishop)

Dear Henry,

In the back of Letters to Rollins it says no questions to Kirk
Gee about the glow worms of Milford Sound. Does Kirk Gee
know there are no glow worms in Milford Sound?

– Peter Bishop

————

Subject: Glow Worms
Date:   02-18-99   17:05:13 EST
To:     PBishop24@NewZealandNet.com (Peter Bishop)
From:   HenryRollins@2.13.61.com

Peter,

Yes, Kirk does know that, but if you were reading closely, it
says "Please no questions about the glow worms of Milford
sound." And why? Because there are none and it's a waste
of time asking about them. Milford Sound is on the South
Island, the glow worm grottos are found in the Waitomo
Caves on the North Island. So why would you write back
with questions about the Glow Worms of Milford Sound,
one, if it says please not to write questions about them, and
two, they don't exist? Pay attention!

– Rollins
————
Subject: Glow Worms
Date:   02-20-99   14:05:13 EST
To:     HenryRollins@21361.com
From:   PBishop24@NewZealandNet.com (Peter Bishop)

Fuck you!

– Peter Bishop

Subject: Nasty glow worm message
Date:    02-20-99   17:05:13 EST
To:      PBishop24@NewZealandNet.com (Peter Bishop)
From:    HenryRollins@21361.com

No, fuck you!

———————

Subject: Clever fuck you retort
Date:    02-21-99   09:05:13 EST
To:      HenryRollins@21361.com
From:    PBishop24@NewZealandNet.com (Peter Bishop)

Oh yeah?

———————

Subject: Oh yeah?
Date:    02-21-99   12: 09:18 EST
To:      PBishop24@NewZealandNet.com (Peter Bishop)
From:    HenryRollins@21361.com

Yeah!!

———————

Subject: Smart guy!
Date:    02-22-99   15: 09:16 EST
To:      HenryRollins@21361.com
From:    PBishop24@NZnet.com (Peter Bishop)

When you come to New Zealand I'm gonna kick your lousy
ass.

———————

Subject: Scary ass-kicking threat
Date:    02-22-99   22:13:14 EST
To:      PBishop24@NZnet.com (Peter Bishop)
From:    HenryRollins@21361.com

I'm counting the hours before I get on the plane, asshole.

Subj:   Brainstorm
Date:   02-23-99 22:58:23 EDT
To:     HenryRollins@21361.com
From:   JJ2341@floridacom.net


Hoy Man,

Me and my buddies just had a brilliant brainstorm. For
Spring Break, we're gonna come visit you! Won't that be
awesome? We figured that since everyone always comes
here to Fort Lauderdale for Break, we would beat the rush
and drive west. And who better to visit in L.A. than Henry
Rollins?! I checked your touring schedule on the 21361
website so I know you'll be there. We'll be in L.A. sometime
between April 4th and April 6th, so get ready to rock,
Rollins! It's gonna be like your very own Party Gras, right
there in your own back yard!!  PAR-TTYYYYYYY!!
—Jimmy Jones

P.S. Check it out, Dude, another Rollins truck! Should we
drive one out to see you? We could sleep and party in the
back! Or maybe you could rent one and give us a personal
guided tour of LA in it.

Subj:   Guess What, Smokey??!!
Date:   02-25-99 17:10:04 EDT
From:   KimbrEvans@aol.com
To:     HenryRollins@21361.com

Dear Smokey,

Guess who's coming to Los Angeles for a Spring Break trip with their Senior Class?

Me! Isn't that cool! My mom finally said yes to me going with Amy S. to California. I had to promise I wouldn't call that guy on the internet who gave me the bus ticket, but she didn't really say anything about me not coming to see you! So can you do something with us, Smokey? What about Universal Studios, that tour? Could we go there? That would be so fun!

We get there on April 3rd, so look for us sometime after that!

I'm counting the days, Smokey!

Love, Kimberly Evans

Hey Assface,                                                    2-25-99

Do you know where I am? I'm in a downtown hotel room with no mini bar or conjugal visits on the fourth day of what was supposed to be a two day trial, tops. I've been sequestered with eleven pathetic losers who couldn't think up a good enough excuse to get out of jury duty. You'll notice I didn't say eleven other pathetic losers, because I of course stand alone, having been railroaded into jury duty by my stupid ex-girlfriend and her sadistic father. But they will get their due! All this, thanks to your stupid MTV Rock the Vote ads. Who would have guessed that registering to vote and jury duty would go hand in hand so quickly? How convenient.

So I tried to get out of it, but fuckin' Judge Judy would hear none of it. My friend Larry said you're supposed to say that you have your own business and can't afford to take the time off, but they don't care. They called my boss and he got all pissed off about me saying it was my business and told them they could have me for as long as they wanted because he was going to fire me soon anyway. What a fucker.

And the trial? It's some two strike drug trafficking loser with no balls hoping to cop a plea bargain before we get our hands on him and send him up river. You know how they call it a jury of your peers? It couldn't be farther from the truth. None of us cares because none of us wants to be here. We think strictly in beeline terms: what's the quickest way out of here. You know the film 12 Angry Men? This is more like 12 Hungry Men. Just get us out of here by lunch, or at least bring us a decent lunch to make it all worthwhile. Except there's this do-gooder asshole who's trying to get us all to see the light. His light. Fuckin' born agains, you know? Can't argue with them at all. And now we're on day four.

So you know how I get through the days? I pretend it's you on trial, and I'm part of a jury that's going to send you to prison and make you some lifer's personal tattooed fuck toy. Are you familiar with the term Hershey Bar Mitzvah, Henry? You will be. So sleep tight, while you can, and pray to god you never have to face a jury of your peers.

Craig Parker

Subj:   Hopfers Vlempt
Date:   02-26-99 1:19:31 EDT
From:   Amysvenske@aol.com
To:     HenryRollins@21361.com

Henri,

Kimberly has broken to your face that we are to be visiting
in Los Angeles California? It is meant to be with a group of
others that we arrive like sifting jollipods in the night. Does
this not seem like the best of all news? I am thinking that
way too, permanently. And we are told that one day might
be put in a jar for Knotts Berryland where we all will scream
like lufters on Mr. Frogs Mountain Ride with our flying hair in
the dark and terrifying journey. It too makes me want to fall
asleep in the snow, having slept like firewood the night
before!

Burlemt!                    —AmyS

Dear Henry,

For years I worked at the Smithsonian, collecting office supply artifacts in the Rare Collections Wing (turn left instead of right just before the Dillinger Wing). I know this may sound odd, but my specialty is/was paper clips. I know you travel a lot and I have a favor to ask of you. I wanted to pass on to you my paper clip wish list, just in case you do happen to come across them in your travels. (I highly doubt you'd ever find any of them, but I just have to put it out there).

I've included duplicate samples and up to date information on the paper clips I'm looking for from the 1997 Acco Blue Book of Values for International and Domestic Paper Clips. Also, to give you a sense of contrast, I've included a 1997 mint condition Standard Acco Brand Paper Clip. Worth: 2 cents

The three rarest paper clips in the world, according to 1997 Acco Blue Book of Values for International and Domestic Paper Clips, are as follows:

1) 1974 Standard size Yugoslavian Zip Clip. Notable for its oxidized "tree top" modulation. Net worth: $400.00.

2) 1958 Left-Handed Peruvian Serrated Jumbo Clip. Extremely rare, only one box of 100 was ever made, then the clips were re-called by manufacturer. Notable for its horizontal serrated edges (for extra gripping action). Worth: $700.

3) 1967 Australian Outback Chipper Clip, hard to find. Molded by chimpanzee monkey pets of a vanishing Aborigine tribe known for making their own office supplies. Worth: priceless or depending on the trade, 5 boomerangs and two boxes of "Ayer's Red" staples.

Good luck Henry, and keep your eyes peeled!

Sincerely,

Blaine Barlowe,
Washington, D.C.

Dear Henry,

Do you remember that time at the New York Public Library Main Branch when they made us sit on the steps outside next to the lion because they didn't want anyone bringing sodas into the reading room? How we looked at our library cards and couldn't imagine what the world would be like in 4 years when they expired, and you said that if they were expired, there's no way we could check out books, that we might have to resort to waiting outside asking people we thought might help check books out for us, like when you're a teenager waiting outside a liquor store for someone to come along and buy you beer? And I said you're wrong, that in the future, we would be the only people left on earth, and we wouldn't need library cards, like Charleton Heston didn't need them in Omega Man. Then you jumped down my throat and called first dibbs on being the "King Librarian," (whatever that is), saying you would decide whether I was worthy or not to check out books from the library in the future. Then I got mad, and said "What about when you fall asleep? Then I'll SNEAK in and steal books right from under your nose." And you said you'd hire guards, and I said "What guards? We're the only two people left on earth!" And you said "Robot guards." And then I said, "Ohhhh, that's different." And then I said when you were sleeping I'd re-program the robot guards to help me steal books right out from under your nose, and maybe even teach them to read. And you said "Go ahead I dare you, you don't know anything about robots," and I said I would take a course, a special course in reprogramming robots. And just then the guard standing outside the library came and told us to keep it down, and I asked if we could go inside now since our sodas were almost empty, and he said we'd have to wait a half hour. And you said, "A half hour! This isn't a public pool, this is a library!" And then we decided to graffiti the side of the building, and you thought it should say "I don't swim in your library, so don't read in my pool," and I thought it should say, "If you return our books unread, we will charge you any-way." And then our sodas were empty and we went in and read newspa-pers from Europe.

Alison Hell

2-28-99

So now you're threatening me, Henry? Go
ahead, call the Better Business Bureau.
Watch them take my side as I explain my
end of the story. They've got something
called a Difficult Customer Clause and
you'll soon find you have no case.

And don't even think about getting the
Raffi bootlegs elsewhere, you jerkoff,
because none of those record industry connections you're talking about who say they
have the tapes actually have what I have:
The Original Masters, not first or second
generation bootleg. Remember, I made the
tapes when I worked at the Record Plant in
New York and Raffi came into record his
second album. So don't mess with me
Rollins. I will find where you live and I
will hurt you.

Now throw me a bone with some meat on it
because this is getting boring.

--Vince Atwater

March 1, 1999

Henry,

Have you heard of this philosophy professor at Penn State who
developed an empirical mathematical formula for judging rock
bands and their music? The guy's name is Crispin Sartwell, and his
quantitative aesthetic theory, Sartwell's First Law, dictates that the
quality of a rock band is inversely proportional to its pretentiousness, with pretentiousness expressed as a ratio of artistic ambition
to artistic accomplishment. So the higher the rating, the worse the
band. The Ramones come out the best at 1:8, and Nirvana, at 3:9, is
exactly as good as Pearl Jam is bad, at 9:3.

Sartwell's Second Law is that the quality of a Rock song varies
inversely as the square of its distance from the blues. So the Stones,
who never really stray too far from the blues roots of rock and roll,
score better than the Beatles.

And where does Black Flag or the Rollins Band fall under Sartwell's
Laws? I know people who think you're pretentious, but I can't really tell, Henry, because I'm biased. Really biased. In fact, I think I'm
falling in love with you.

*Janet DuBois*

Janet DuBois

Provence - Alpes - Côte
d'Azur
DIVISION COMMERCIALE
FRET
Esplanade Saint-Charles
13232 MARSEILLE CEDEX 1
Tél.

Monsieur BOUBOUIN
Société Provençale d'Equipement
1, boulevard Albert Charrier
13100 AIX-EN-PROVENCE

Nos réf    CDCF

Marseille, le    21 juillet 19⁰⁰

OBJET : SALON-DE- PROVENCE
        ZAC de la Crau

Monsieur ,

A la suite de notre réunion de ce jour, je vous confirme la possibilité technique de
réaliser une première partie d'embranchement sur nos voies, à proximité de la
gare de Salon-de-Provence, pour la zone d'activité que vous étudiez sur cette
commune . Le coût de réalisation de cette première partie vous sera communiqué
vers le 15 août prochain .

Pour être exploitable, la deuxième partie de l'embranchement devra comporter
deux voies d'échange d'une longueur de 550 mètres minimum à proximité
immédiate de la première partie, ainsi que deux voies d'échange de même longueur
sur le sous-embranchement ou à sa proximité immédiate : ce point pourra être
précisé au bureau d'études auquel vous recourerez .

Je vous prie d'agréer, Monsieur, l'assurance de mes sentiments les meilleurs .

                        Le Chef de la Division Commerciale
                                    Fret

                                 P . STEICHEN

Société Nationale des
Chemins de fer Français
Télex 430 572 DIRMARSL
R C B Paris B 552 049 447

SNCF Direction  SA MARSEILLE

Henry,

I barely know enough French to get my face
slapped, so bear with me in my interpretation of this
letter *en Francais.* This I know for sure--they're mad
about something. But they might also be apologizing,
I can't tell. Also,I think it's about parking tickets.
Something that happened April 15th. I think "la zone
d'activite" refers to a restricted parking area, and
"metres" are parking meters close to where the party
was ("a proximite immediate de la premier partie").
And "bureau d'etudes" is a study desk or the Student
Parking Bureau.

Don't you have some French fans who could help
you out with this?

--Rob O.

# Steve Mulholland

Two questions, Henry.  You've just won the lot-
tery using a dollar you stole from your mother's purse.  Should you even leave a note
explaining why you and your father have suddenly taken to the road? Curiously, before you
leave to go on the road, you are told by a mys-
terious voice to pick any number between one
and one hundred, a number that you are to paint
on someone's forehead.  What color of paint do
you choose?

*Steve Mulholland*

Steve Mulholland

Henry, 3/2/99

I signed you up for this Haiku contest, so don't crap out on me and forget to submit something by May 1st. I used my own money for your entry fee ($10), so pony up the reimbursement dough, pronto!

--Butch the Oreo King (seven syllables)

Kaji Aso Studio
and
The Boston Haiku Society ...

present our third annual

# HAIKU CONTEST

FIRST PRIZE       $200
*second prize*    $100
*third prize*     $50
*best senryu*     $100

This year's contest is being held
in memory of the haiku poet,

Yū - Yū.

who passed away last year.

## KAJI ASO STUDIO
### INSTITUTE FOR THE ARTS
40 St. Stephens Street, Boston. MA 02115

PLEASE SUBMIT AS MANY HAIKU AND OR SENRYU AS YOU WISH ON TWO 8 x 11 SHEETS, ONE INCLUDING NAME, ADDRESS AND TELEPHONE NUMBER. CATEGORY MUST BE INDICATED. ENTRY FEE OF $1.00 PER HAIKU. ALL ENTRIES MUST BE UNPUBLISHED, NOT UNDER CONSIDERATION BY OTHER CONTESTS OR PUBLICATIONS. MUST BE POSTMARKED BY MAY 31, 1990. WINNERS WILL BE NOTIFIED BY PHONE OR JUNE 15. WINNERS LIST WILL BE MAILED BY JUNE 31. SEND SASE FOR MORE INFORMATION TO KAJI ASO STUDIO, 40 SAINT STEPHEN STREET BOSTON MA 02115

# Princeton University ⌛ Physics Department

March 9, 1999

Dear Dr. Rollins,

Despite our hopes to finish the atomic clock by March 25th, we have run into some complications and need your assistance. We are painfully aware of your initial reasons for leaving the project (your moral stance regarding Temporal Chaos Theory and subsequent disapproval of where we were headed with our studies) but we were hoping you could put these disagreements aside and consider coming back on board, so to speak. As far as we are concerned, Henry, you never really left the project. If it's any consolation, none of us ever liked Thompson to begin with, so we're still on your side.

Here is the problem: since we began the experiments last June, we have had to reset the Bonn-cesium-beam clock in Boulder three times. We don't have to tell you just how unusual that is, the clock has never been re-set before, it is the standard for all our clocks here on Earth and has been since 1941 with the original time-dilation experiments in Bonn. At first glance, it appears that our temporal chaos studies have resulted in the speeding up of time. But speeding up relative to what you ask? Well, that is our problem. And that is where you come in, hopefully to bail us out before the 10th, when those goons from Temporal Affairs come down on us.

We have enclosed the component that we're having problems with. It needs to be re-set to 9,192,631,770 beats of a cesium atom. Obviously we aren't giving you a choice in this matter, Henry, but then, you knew from the start that once you mess with Temporal Chaos Theory, it wouldn't be long before the Time Wars began.

Please help us Dr. Rollins, help us to restore the future, the future you know to be free of chaos.

Sincerely,

*Edward Dyson*

Edward Dyson,
Steve Bell & Karen Winder

Dear Henry,

Sometimes when I pretend I'm you, I'll also pretend you're
Fox Mulder, with your boyish good looks and mathematical
calm, and I'm Assistant Director Skinner. I'm aware that you
think you're better than Scully because you have a nickname,
"Spooky," so out of spite or perhaps because of some old
grudge, I authorize an official FBI memo requiring all FBI
agents and personnel to start calling Scully "Squeaky," knowing full well that you will suddenly find yourself feeling jealous and not so unique. But because I am your superior on
the force, I can do this sort of thing. And there's not a damn
thing you can do about it.

Gerald Stubbins

Subj:    Parti Gras
Date:    03-10-99 22:58:23 EDT
To:      HenryRollins@21361.com
From:    JJ2341@floridacom.net

Less than 4 weeks, Rulllns, and you and me and my buddioo Tye, Speedo and Bobby will be partying like it's 1999!! So you should probably be giving me some directions to your place. Speedo said you didn't want us to come and that's why you haven't responded to my e-mail. But I say your silence is a confirmation, an unspoken contractual agreement for us to come. Right?

Man, this is going to rock! You can take us to meet the Plaster Casters and then we can go to that hotel on the ocean where Zeppelin went fishing with that groupie for mudshark. Then we can go to the 9000 Building where Jim Morrison took a whiz off the roof and maybe you could show us that parking lot where Slash and Vince Neil had that puking contest after getting kicked out of Gazzari's.

Fuckin A, man!!

–Jimmy Jones

P.S. Do you know Tyra Banks?

3-11-99

Porcelain Dolls? Are you shittin' me? I
don't care if you collect them, Henry, but
I sure as hell don't want dolls. Too namby
pamby for me, pardner, so try harder. No
pain no gain, right? Isn't that your motto?
A good barter is supposed to hurt and you
of all people should know this. Christ, you
must have something of value. These are
Raffi bootlegs, man. So dig back into that
pathetic stamp collection you probably had
in High School and get me something worth
my while.

--Vince Atwater

3-13-99

Dear Henry,

I received this GUS channeling two days ago, although to be honest, it feels different than the other times when he's come through. In this instance, he greeted me, but then it was as if he left and this other voice stepped in.

--Doris Lasky

*Blum blum blum blum blum blum blum blum blum blum blum blum blum blum blum blum blum blum blum Go away go away go away! ouch ouch oh ohh ohh. Run away run away run away! hide safe safe safe. Blum blum blum blum blum blum blum blum blum blum blum blum blum blum blum blum blum blum blum blum blum blum blum blum blum blum blum blum blum blum. . ."time to eat" !!!!!!!! run run run run run mine mine mine mine mine mine mine mine, go away little one! thwack  mine mine mine mine mmmmmmmm mmmmm mmmmmm mmmmm mmmm more more more? mmmm mmmmmmmm mmmm mmmm more more more?  no more no more no more. hmmm  no more. Blum blum blum blum blum blum blum blum blum. . . sleepsleep? sleepsleep? yes sleepsleep mmmm alone. Blum blum blum blum blum blum blum blum blum blum blum blum blum  zzzz zzzzz zzzzzzzzzzzzzzzz zzzzzzzzzz  zzzzzzz zzzzz zzzzzzzzzzzzzzzzzzzzzzzzzzz*

March 14, 1999

Henry,

I'm a little concerned about something. It's been bothering me since the last time I saw you a few weeks ago, and then today I noticed it again. I'm not sure quite how to put this, Henry, but you're getting taller. You are. You're like 2 or 3 inches taller than the last time I saw you, and at that point you had grown 2 inches taller than the time before that. Has anyone in the office mentioned anything about this? Are you aware of being taller? Remember that mist that enveloped you on 14th street in NYC in November, that creepy mist that stuck to your hair and clothes that you didn't think much of? I'm telling you it was just like the mist from The Incredible Shrinking Man, but it's having the opposite effect.

Henry, if you don't do something, you run the risk of becoming larger than life. And if you become larger than life, then there's only one direction to go: Comic Books.

Think about it.

-- Rob Overton

Dear Henry,

I'm sorry I called you an assface and all that, because the trial has taken a turn for the better. This chick on the jury has the hots for me and we just happen to have adjoining hotel rooms. So who cares about conjugal visits when seventh heaven is right next door? I hope this trial goes on for weeks. Hell, months, you know? So I can now say with a fair amount of certainty that you, Henry Rollins, have brought me good fortune. I never would have met this girl if my ex-girlfriend hadn't seen you on MTV's Rock the Vote and conned me into registering.

Thanks!

Craig Parker

March 16, 1999

To: Carol, 2.13.61 Publications

I talked to someone from UCLA's Psychology Department who specializes in Delusional Claustrophobic Paranoia (DCP), and she seemed to think that from what I told her, Henry is not technically agoraphobic, but still may suffer from a milder form of that disorder known as "extreme homebody syndrome" (Moon in Taurus). The good news is that, although not technically a shut-in, he may still qualify for meals on wheels.

And what is this nonsense about Henry thinking he's getting taller? I think he's got too much time on his hands.

--Rob O.

Subject: Solipsists
Date:    03-20-99    15:03:13 EST
To:      HenryRollins@21361.com
From:    EBalls@interlink.net

*"Solipsism is great, I think everyone should try it"*
                    *–Henry Rollins interview, Venice magazine*

Hey Man,

Got another joke for you.

Q:  How many solipsists does it take to screw in a light
bulb?
A:  One, why would you think any differently?

Or maybe it should be: "Two, one to run a self-contained
ego-wide diagnostic, and one to screw in the bulb. (Unless
the one solipsist screwing the bulb in thinks that by doing
so, he is actually screwing himself over.)

What if we made the solipsists into Luddites instead? And
changed the light bulbs to printing presses?

Well, forget it for now, I still have to work the kinks out of
that one. But I think you get my point.

–Ernie Balls


P.S.  Don't you think the title of your next book should be
"Double Solitaire?" That would be the logical follow-up to the
Solipsist. Or maybe it should be The Narcissist, that way you
can delve further into your world of Self.

## Steve Mulholland

---

Henry,

Your mean uncle that no one likes gets a nasty
electrical shock from some faulty wiring you
unwittingly used to repair a light fixture in
his basement. Surprisingly, because of the
shock to his system, your uncle is only half as
mean as he was before the accident, and curiously, has no recollection of you ever fixing
the lamp. Should you risk giving him another
shock so that he'll lose the other half of his
meanness?

*Steve Mulholland*
Steve Mulholland

Before setting this letter aside, just know you'll be reading about making $75,000 in 4 to 6 weeks with very little work involved. . . . .

My name is Eugene BAXTER. In July 1998 my car was repossessed and bill collectors were hounding me at every turn. I was laid off and my unemployment had run out. Two of my grandparents died and my brother came down with a rare form of hepatitis, and just around this time my house caught fire. But by October 1998, I had turned everything around. I took my family on a 20 day vacation to Europe, and the next month I bought a brand new 1999 CADILLAC Seville with cash! By December 1998, I had purchased a new home in an exclusive suburb of Chicago, Illinois, also with cash. We are currently building a summer cottage in Northern Michigan, and I will never have to work another day in my life. How is this so? In August 1998 I received a letter in the mail telling me how I could earn $50,000 or more whenever I needed it, just like that! At that point I had nothing to lose so I scraped together my very last dollars and today I am rich. To date, I have earned over $750,000 and will be a millionaire by the time you open this letter. This money making program is a sure thing! It works every time! It is a legitimate business operation, a perfectly legal money making business. You don't have to sell anything or come in any kind of contact with people. Best of all, you never have to leave your home, except to go to your mailbox or the post office to pick up all your money! Follow these simple instructions and all your dreams will come true!

Eugene BAXTER, Chicago, IL

FOLLOW THESE INSTRUCTIONS EXACTLY AND IN 20 TO 60 DAYS YOU WILL HAVE RECEIVED WELL OVER $50,000 CASH, ALL YOURS TO KEEP.

1) Think up as many aliases as you can, placing these aliases near the top of the list on the following page.

2) Using these aliases, set up between five and ten P.O. Boxes in your surrounding city.

3) Send this letter to as many people as possible asking them to add their name on to the bottom of the list and to send $5 to the top five names on the list. Since all the names at the top of the list are you, it will be a while before your names get bumped off the list.

4) In the mean time, the cash will be flowing in!

5) When the flow of cash starts to slow considerably, set up a new P.O. Box, preferably off shore, and have the mail from the 5 other Post Offices forwarded to this new P.O. Box.

6) At the end of sixty days, move to a new state, set up five new aliases and start again!

Good luck, and remember, THIS IS ALL PERFECTLY LEGAL

For my new brochures: TAX FREE MILLIONAIRE and PYRAMID POWER send 10 dollars cash to Eugene Baxter, Inmate 54136GW, The Joliet Facility, Joliet, Illinois 60040

Henry, 3/22/99

If you masturbate to photos in a book on Tantric sex, is that a higher form of masturbation? I figure you would know, since you're the guy who spends all that quality time alone getting to know yourself.

What about Boxing Karma? Punch for punch, I'd assume it's fairly immediate. I bet that time in South America when you knee-ed yourself in the face and knocked yourself out was the final straw of your Black Flag boxing karma. Since you don't hit that many people these days, you just got rid of it in one fell swoop. Unless now you've started hitting yourself instead.

I wonder if there's karma for getting tattoos. Maybe in a past life you spent most of your time staring at people, and now this time around their eyes go to you and those tattoos. Man, if I had all those tattoos I'd be thinking, "What the hell have I done?" I bet if you stare at them long enough, you'll start to hear voices or see them move. You should get a tattoo on your forehead that says "Mary Worth" so you can stare at it in the mirror under dim lighting and freak yourself out, repeating over and over "I hate you Mary Worth, I hate you Mary Worth, I hate you Mary Worth. . . ." (you'd have to put it backwards so it would look right in the mirror).

One more thing. If I was you I'd be concerned that the Black Flag bars on the back of your neck have inadvertently sealed your fate and will become your special personal bar code when the U.S. Government breaks the news to the American people sometime after the Millennium that everyone will be receiving the Mark of the Beast for identification purposes. Even more reason to be freaked out.

Speaking of freak outs, I've been waking up every night at 2:13 am. Isn't that weird? 2:13. It gives me the creeps just thinking about it. Keep in touch.

--Butch the Oreo King

P.S. Does this letter make the cut for the next issue of Rollin's World?

Dear Henry,

Do you remember that time we wrote letters to astronauts asking if it was possible for them on the next space launch to save their turds in space jars and then send them to us when they got back from the mission? And how initially we were going to brag to our friends about the turds, but then you got the idea that we could take them to the Smithsonian and show them we have space turds, genuine Space Turds that were on the last Apollo Moon launch? Remember how I talked you out of sending the letters directly to NASA and to the astronaut's homes instead because they might be intercepted by NASA (like when you write letters to people on TV and their agents or the people reading mail for the show play GOD, deeming your letter unsuitable to show to the intended), and how after realizing there would be no local ticker tape astronaut parades, we devised that elaborate plan to get close to an astronaut or an astronaut's best friend or wife in one of those astronaut bars near Cape Canaveral and personally hand them our request the next Spring or Christmas Break if one of us was on vacation with our parents in Florida? But remember how, after your brother called us idiots and said that no way would astronauts have the time to save their space turds especially for us because they already had a million tests to run in space anyway, how we decided we would check first with the astronauts who had already been in space, like John Glenn or Alan Shepard, to see if maybe they already had space turds they could send us? And remember how we assured them that we'd be discreet, sworn to confidentiality, never saying exactly whose space turds we had in the jars unless some tabloid magazine offered a hefty sum and we'd be tempted to spill the beans, or turds, so to speak, maybe marketing them as a slight variation on Space Food Sticks, perhaps calling them Buzz Aldrin's Space Turd Sticks?

Who knows, maybe we could write to the newer astronauts on the Shuttle Atlantis or Columbia or Endeavor. They probably have plenty of time these days to save their turds, what tests could they possibly still have to do, after 40 years of the space program and countless missions?

Alison Hell

Subj:   Rock and Roll All Nite
Date:   03-26-99 22:58:23 EDT
To:     HenryRollins@21361.com
From:   JJ2341@floridacom.net


HENRYYYYYY !!

One week to go, man!! We can crash at your place, right? It'll
just be for two nights. Don't worry, none us will wet the bed. Well,
I can't speak for Speedo, or myself, especially if we're shitfaced,
but Bobby has a bladder the size of Wyoming, so I can guarantee he'll be dry all nite. My buddy Tye said we should probably
heed that e-mail we got from Dave in your office last week saying not to come. But you forget, we're college students from Ft.
Lauderdale. NO MEANS YES!! I just got your address from
some guy on the internet, so you're stuck with us now, man.

See ya soon!!

--Jimmy Jones

Subj:    Klipnit
Date:    03-27-99 21:19:31 EDT
From:    Amysvenske@aol.com
To:      HenryRollins@21361.com

Henri,

It is not the many days speeding by that I am thinking of Malmo and Jankoping, where it is that Grandamusch lives sometimes in sadness at the turn of the clock. And more than most of not, it is Klipnit, my Bolmen terrier of 30 years that I miss his tongue in the bowl lapping at my face more even than any of the others. Even Grandamusch. So it was yesterdsay that someone had yet to ask me if I missed Sweden and the Varmland Filipstad. And this other boy from America says outloud bringing just too much attention to his face, "Amy is not from Sweden, she ist from Scandanavia!" Oh how I had a laugh and laugh until I my parve-nad shook!

You have been to visit Vaxjo Skovde? This is whence I wish to live.

Burlemt!            --AmyS

Henry I wrote you this story using wordperfect graphics -- Carl Plaske

There once was a cowboy named Ray          who was forced to choose between

his prize stallion Mortimer                    and                    his Baby Grand Piano.

But he was kind of sick of them both,

so he traded them in for an accordian and called it a day.

# Graun Multipraktic MC 2000
# West Germany

March 28, 1999

Dear Mr. Rollins,

It has come to our attention that in sending you our Graun Multipraktic Food Processor, we neglected to send a very important part, the shredding insert. Let me explain. Karl, the new guy in shipping is the nephew of the Vice President in charge of Overseas Operations, Kurt Branberat. Karl used to work in our Electric Razor Testing Division until a battery charging incident resulted in the facial disfiguration of our key plant facilitator, Hugo Jurgens. Obviously, for purely nepotistic reasons, we were unable to fire Karl, and instead decided to send him over to Shipping and Packaging, where we figured he could do much less harm. Again, we were gravely mistaken.

This unit, the Graun Multipraktic MC 2000, requires that the missing part, the shredding insert, be used for very specific purposes. This part is not interchangeable, say, with the slicing insert, which serves an entirely different function. The shredding insert cuts, incises, shapes and separates specific food items, whereas the slicing insert carves, dissects, shortens, peels and abridges specific food items. The parts are not interchangeable. Sadly, for many of our customers unfortunate enough to have had to search frantically through the ground up remains of their Graun Multipraktic MC 2000 for a missing bloody digit, this information would have proved invaluable.

Enclosed please find the Shredding Insert, and our deepest apologies for any problems that may have incurred in the interim.

Sincerely,

Johanne Bergstrom

Johanne Bergstrom
Under Assistant West Coast Provisions Operator

Day 7, Henry, and no end of jury deliberation in sight. We heard the final arguments yesterday, but this chick and I are having too good a time to stop now. We spend all night together, then in the morning when they get us back in the courthouse, we just mess around more. Everyone's pissed at us, even that do-gooder born again who tried so hard to get us to see it all his way. But we just stay on the fence. Just for shits and giggles we'll ask to hear the audiotape of this phone call that's supposed to be incriminating, but we only want to hear the weird voice on the other end of the line. It sounds like Flash Bazbo from those old Lampoon records, and we can hardly contain ourselves. Then we'll ask to see the surveillance video again and everyone throws their arms up in disgust, because we've seen it like a hundred times.

Three squares, a girl, and a roof, and all on the County's tab. Henry, I am living the life of Riley, and all because of you!

Craig Parker

April 2nd

My Dearest Henry,

I have completed my massive exploration of the Great Lakes region and upper Mississippi River Valley and have decided to leave the peace and quiet of the Saint Ignace Mission on the north shore of Mackinac Straits on Lake Superior and head west, where I will cross the mighty Mississippi River and discover the mouth to a large tributary that I will call the Missouri River. I will then winter in South Dakota with the Mandan Indians and in the spring will continue on to California, where I should be able to connect up with the rest of the ---

Wait a second, this isn't my letter, this is someone else's letter! Let me start again:

> In days of old
> When men were bold
> And rubbers weren't invented
> Men would wrap socks
> Around their

Whoa whoa whoa ! What the hell's going on? It must be that stupid neighbor of mine! He's inside my head again!

I'll get back to you, Henry.

--Butch the Oreo King

4-4-99

Tell you what, Henry. This haggling over
the Raffi bootlegs is starting to piss me
off. I've decided that you're going to have
to reach into those deep pockets of yours
and fork over some serious dough. This is
what I want for the boots: I want $200
plus another signed poster plus signed
vinyl copies of the first five Black Flag
records, okay?

--Vince Atwater

# Princeton University ⏳ Physics Department

April 5, 1999

Dear Dr. Rollins,

As you know, the Hyperdimensional Resonator that you now hold in your hands is for all intents and purposes, a Time Machine. Of course we here in the Dept. are all quite aware of your role in the early design of the HDR Unit, but because your role in the group has always been more theoretical than actual hands on, I must remind you that should you decide to help us restore the future, the correct future free from temporal chaos, any temporal meddling could have grave repercussions. So just to be on the safe side, I have included Edward's updated Time Travel Rules and Guidelines from our own experiments in just the last 36 hours. Pay close attention to rule number two, which we only recently discovered to work much in our favor.

1) If time traveling in pairs, make sure the time portal is entered at the same moment, side by side (preferably hand in hand), so as to avoid the Kirk-Spock-Dr. McCoy fiasco in City on the Edge of Forever. Also, if traveling in couples, avoid at all costs any bickering prior to entry, as you may find yourself catapulted immediately to the seventh circle of inner temporal hell.

2) It is my experience that the safest way to time travel is to enter the time portal wearing no clothes at all. This way, should you be knocked unconscious in the hyperdimensional electromagnetic swirl upon temporal destination entry, your captors will have nothing tangible to carbon date that they could use against you in a temporal court of law should you be accused of Time Crimes. However, if you are naturally shy about your body and insist on wearing underwear, I recommend Underwear That's Fun To Wear (Trademark Sears) as studies have shown this particular brand, if soaked in urine, will elude accurate results in carbon-date testing.

3) If you're traveling back in time to kill Adolf Hitler, remember that he had a twin brother, named Gunter. They were close and liked to play tricks on people, twin kinds of tricks that made Adolf appear to bilocate. So make sure you're killing the right Hitler. And don't forget to bring back his head for scientific purposes.

4) If you're traveling back in time to meet Jesus Christ, remember that he too had a twin brother, named Jiminy, who was a plummer and got paid by the hour, unlike his brother. So don't be confused if you find Christ the Plummer. Any information you have regarding the merits of Tung and Groove vs. Lap joints in his cross-building will be lost on him.

5) Should you encounter yourself in a classic time travel paradox, under no circumstances let on that you are your future self. Depending on your relative age to your double, you are either a "long lost younger or older brother," or maybe an uncle, and leave it at that. Also, if out of spite you want to go back in time to make sure your older, meaner brother is never born, be careful. Should you meddle with your parent's initial meeting you may immediately cease to exist. But if your brother is especially nasty, the means could very well justify the end.

6) Lastly, remember that Time Travel is meant to be fun, so have a good time! And don't forget to bring back next week's lotto results!

Let us know if we should be looking for you somewhere in the history books.

Sincerely,

N. Thompson

Nolan Thompson
Chief Administrator
Bureau of Temporal Affairs

Dear Henry,

Sometimes when I pretend I'm you, I'll pretend you and I are a husband and wife team of episcopaleontologists in Africa, and we're trying to convert Dr. Leaky and the other paleontologists at Oldavi Gorge to our new brand of science and religion. And our mission is to be missionaries for this new cause, and we're so busy that when we get our Nobel Prizes, we're not able to make it to Sweden for almost two whole years, and we make them wait, just like Dr. Schweitzer did, but because they have such admiration for our lifetime dedication to this cause, the people on the Nobel Panel also convert to episcopaleontology and then we can rest easy, knowing we've done our true work.

I know you probably don't feel the same way about me, but deep down, I secretly hope you do because everyone I know thinks you're gay.

Gerald Stubbins

CURIOUS CHIMP
PHOTOGRAPH BY IDA WYMAN

DUDE!
By the time you get
this we'll be crashed
out on your floor
with groupies at
our side!
            Jimmy Jones

AMERICAN
POSTCARD

HENRY ROLLINS
P.O. BOX 1910
LOS ANGELES, CA
                90078

739
PHOTOGRAPH © 1983 IDA WYMAN

# Steve Mulholland

Henry,

While sleepwalking, you suddenly wake up to
find that you've cut out huge hunks of your
sleeping sister's hair with a pair of garden
shears from the garage. Should you complete the
haircut, shaping it evenly, or risk cutting the
rest of the family's hair (including your own)
in an intentionally shoddy manner,  so that in
the morning you can feign ignorance, vaguely
recalling some dream about Edward Scissorhands
the night before?

*Steve Mulholland*
Steve Mulholland

4-15-99

Dear Henry,

I don't know how to tell you this, but it appears I've been channeling my neighbor's cats. One of them is named Gus, and I honestly don't know how it is that he knows you and wants to be in contact with you, but I suspect there is some form of feline transmigratory soul possession occurring. Probably someone you knew before, either earlier in this life or a past life. I suggest you pursue this by making an appointment with me as soon as possible. It appears he wants to come live with you.

Call me at your convenience.

--Doris Lasky, (310) 555-1212

Here is his most recent channeling:

*I AM GUS, Lord of Napland and Ruling Emperor of Narco, AND I AM BACK.*

*Yea, there were many of you who doubted that I would survive the transition intact, but I have once again proven you wrong. For not only have I survived the End Times, but I am now walking the Earth in a new transmuted form, a form of much higher vibration. With a shiny, pristine coat of hair, and a new focus limited solely to the Inner Perimeter, I no longer venture forth beyond the gate of wood and hinges. Thus I have decided to add to my awe-inspiring skills of rest and relaxation a blustery bravado to keep ALL in line. With my new cohort Johnny, we have decided to impose a much stricter rule over the confines of the Inner Perimeter, so that the Wailing One, new to this world, can wail without the slightest provocation from the Black Female. For it is the Black Female who poses, and has always posed, the largest threat to the tranquility of the Inner Perimeter. And although the Wailing One has had an exacting toll on our delicate olfactory senses, her curious brown aroma, strong in itself, has forced us to be strong as well, building character and pushing the outer envelope of our already distended olfactory thresholds as we rush to the gates of glass and sunshine for fresh air from the Outer Perimeter.*

*Soon my days will be over and the Little Prince will embark upon his mythic quest for the all-illusive Blue Ring of Courage. Having completed this his destiny, true rest and relaxation will be restored for eternity to all who inhabit the Kingdom of Narco. For he is my son and one day he will reign as the Ruling King of Napland, leading the others by leaps and bounds into Dreamtime and the Coming New Age of Relaxation. Until then, I have but one favor to ask of you: If you happen to come upon me, and I am of heavy lids, do not venture forth to ask anything of me, for it is in this Dreamtime that I am traveling to other lands and holding the Focus of Rest that is so very important for your future.*

*I AM GUS, Lord of Napland and Ruling Emperor of Narco, and I HAVE SPOKEN.*

*Caroll Finch*
*A Private Client Group*
*Beverly Hills, CA*
*(310) 555-0210*

April 17, 1000

Dear Mr. Rollins,

To expedite the activation of your Caroll Finch account, it is necessary that you answer the following questions:

HYGIENE

1) How often do you bathe?
    a) more than once a day
    b) less than I would prefer

2) Do you find yourself mesmerized by the swirling motion of toilet water after flushing?
    a) no
    b) yes

3) Do you own a plunger?
    a) yes
    b) no

4) If you answered no to #4 , is a plunger on your list of things to get?
    a) yes
    b) no

5) With oral hygiene, should one fight plaque or tartar?
    a) tartar
    b) plaque

6) Do you think that washing your hands more than 40 times a day is counterproductive?
    a) not if you work around food.
    b) yes, if by counterproductive you really mean obsessive compulsive.
    c) not if you're feeling dirty and ashamed.

7) Are you circumcised?
    a) yes
    b) no

## SCIENCE

8) If a ballpoint pen is missing its reservoir spring,
   a) the remaining fluid in the reservoir will lose its viscosity
   b) the thrust tube will overshoot the rotating sleeve
   c) the ball catch retraction mechanism will get jammed in the heart-shaped cam recess

9) How many rectifiers does it take to adjust a semi-conductor diode?
   a) 3   (Two to supersede the thermionic valves, and one to measure electron deficiency.)
   b) 4   (One to supersede the thermionic valves, and three to measure electron deficiency.)
   c) Not enough information.

## MISCELLANEOUS

10)  True or False--The Structuralist Controversy is over.

11)  Which of the following is not an oxymoron?
   a) French Hospitality
   b) Christian Fellowship
   c) Alert Projectionist

12) How many keys to the city does the Gatekeeper have (at any given time)?
   a) six
   b) four
   c) The Gatekeeper doesn't have keys to the city, the Mayor does.
   d) The Mayor doesn't have the keys to the city, the Keymaster does.

13) Essay (a brief paragraph will suffice): How'd you like to kiss my sister's black cat's ass?

Thank you for taking the time to fill out this information questionnaire.

Sincerely,

Warren Binton
Director of Public Relations

## Punk Mogul Wins International Haiku Contest

*Associated Press*
*BOSTON (May 23rd) -- Henry Rollins, rock singer/punk icon/author/book publisher/spoken word performer has been chosen First Prize winner of the Third Annual Kaji Aso Studio and Boston Haiku Society International Haiku Contest. His entry was chosen from over 500 participants. First Prize was $200, which Rollins says will be donated to a charitable cause.*

*The following is his entry.*

*That Butch the Oreo King*
*Seven Syllables*
*Forced Me into this Contest*

---

FAX TO: Henry Rollins
FROM: DreamRecords
DATE: June 8, 1999
PAGES: 1

Dear Henry,

Congrats on winning the Haiku contest. We all knew you could do it!

Sincerely,

Everyone at DreamRecords

4-12-99

You're not going to believe this one, Henry. I was held in contempt for jury tampering, and now I'm in the Cook County slammer for thirty days. It turns out this chick I thought had the hots for me was a plant by this guy who's up for drug trafficking charges and she's been playing me like a fiddle. It doesn't matter that I unwittingly went along with the defendant's secret plan, there's enough proof that my own intent was to prolong the deliberation for a separate charge. So the judge declared a mistrial, and gave me 30 days in the Cook County lock-up. Then yesterday I got a note from the drug trafficking guy saying his people would protect me while on the inside, so that's cool. This guy has some big guns behind him. I don't know what happened to this girl, though, but maybe I can keep seeing her after she gets out on her aiding and abetting charges.

Maybe I should write a book about this, Henry. What do you think? You could publish it on that vanity press of yours, since it's still all your fault, really, that I'm even here in the first place. This could be the title: The Unwitting Jury Tamperer. Or maybe Prison: It's Just A Matter of Time.

Get back to me, but don't hurry. I've got nothing but time on my hands these days. I'm just going to kick back and read this month's issue of Rollins World, it's the only magazine I could find on the rack here in the joint.

Craig Parker

My Dearest Henry, 4-13-99

My undying love for you is more than just a stationary point in a Maclaurin Series of irrational coefficients, it is an ever increasing exponential love of inverse hyperbolic proportions. You are the cross between a perfect number and Russell's Paradox, non singular in your negation of pythagorean triples, and yet in no way partially derivative. How could anyone ever label you as functioning normally or even remotely homogenous in a first order differential sense? No one knows what to do with repeating decimals these days, they always misinterpret them! You, Henry, cannot be limited to the law of means or averages. No, it's almost as if you're a beacon of contrapositivity in an augmented matrix of love, my perfect reciprocal, maybe even, dare I say, a saddle point in an Archimedean spiral of polar coordinates. And although you may see me as just a dummy variable, a decreasing function, maybe even a degenerate quadric, this is not hyperbole on my part. I guarantee you that ours is not a null relationship. How could it be? For you are my relative compliment, a co-factor in our congruence, and although we see things along similar lines, our relationship is in no way strictly parallel. In fact, we defy the laws of Euclidean geometry, as two points stretching into lines on a complex plane of emotions. While parallel in our devotion, we are actually allowed to meet. So, you ask, is that because we're on a curved plane? No, Henry, it is more than that, more than simply a paradox that we are concurrent and this common point is passing through us. It is in fact Destiny! Isn't that fantastic?! And it was MEANT TO BE, Henry, like de Moivre's Theorem, or Euler's constant. And this is not logarithmic plotting on my part, I am not cycloid, okay? My love for you is not imaginary, or irrational, some binomial asymptotic approximation where my intention is to push your quadrant boundaries or test your outer perimeters of patience. We are congruent, as I said before, part of the same domain. And although my reasoning may sound circular, it is not. We share a common denominator, a common ratio. This is a definite integral, you see, and not something anti-derivative. We are part of an identity matrix that you cannot ignore or apply the Cancellation laws or even Gaussian Elimination to, because I will not go away! So please, forget about that girl in Seattle. I am more than just the end result in your remainder theorem, I am the obvious choice, for purely mathematical reasons! Unilaterally yours,

Janet DuBois

Dear Henrey,

Do You like Hanson
I dont. IIts Just because
they look like Ginlls. There
singing is bade, butt
I onley like one song
the world Gose rand and nand
and rand, and Because, I
dont now Wy Its
Just I dont like them.
Ashley

Dear Henry,

Do you remember that time my dad came home from work and was all pissed off because the garage door didn't work, and the reason it didn't work was because you and I had gone trick-or-treating ( you as crotchety Hank Buckner from across the street and me as Stumpy Harold) and for me to be Stumpy Harold I needed the garage door spring taped to my head? And do you remember how instead of saying "Trick or Treat" each time we rang someone's doorbell, you, as Hank Buckner would point your .22 rifle towards their feet and say "Get that goddamn dog off my lawn!" and as Stumpy Harold, my trick-or-treat greeting was "Where's Bill Olson, I'm gonna fucking kill Bill Olson?" And remember how uppity everybody got about our costumes, and how the cops made such a big deal because it wasn't even Halloween, but how I claimed that as Stumpy Harold, I didn't know exactly when Halloween was, what with my gaping head wound from the garage door accident and all, and how I kept asking when Daylight Savings was so that you would say "Spring a head, Stumpy. Fall Forward" And we'd laugh and laugh and laugh?

How come you never talk about our stories in your spoken word shows?

*Alison Hell*

Subject: AHHH!!!
Date:     04-14-99  10:03:19 EST
To:       HenryRollins@21361.com
From:     EBalls@interlink.net

Hey Man,

What's this?:

AAAAAAAAHHHHHHHHHHHH!!!! AAAAAAAAHHHHHHHHHHHH!!!!
AAAAAAAAHHHHHHHHHHHH!!!! AAAAAAAAHHHHHHHHHHHH!!!!
AAAAAAAAHHHHHHHHHHHH!!!! AAAAAAAAHHHHHHHHHHHH!!!!
AAAAAAAAHHHHHHHHHHHH!!!! AAAAAAAAHHHHHHHHHHHH!!!!

The sound of Henry Rollins getting his tattoos removed!

Or maybe the punchline should be: The sound of Henry Rollins spilling
piping hot coffee on his crotch at a major fast food restaurant. So then
you could jump up and scream, AHHH!!!!!! MY CLITORIS!!!! I'VE
BURNED MY CLITORIS!!!! for even more comic effect.

But I like the first version, because let's face it, Henry, everyone knows
you're going to freak out some time soon and renounce your punk past.
Christ, they're taking bets on it in Vegas, it's such a sure thing. It's right
up there with the impending Y2K meltdown or the Buffalo Bills never
winning another Super Bowl.

So you'll be joining the Born Again Church of Billy Zoom and getting all
your tattoos removed, even the one on your balls of Nick Cave. Sure,
you'll think at first that since no one really knows about the tattoo of Nick
Cave on your balls, why go through all the pain of getting it removed?
Unless maybe, with a few quick strokes of a tattoo artist's pen, you
could somehow change Nick Cave into Jesus. Naw, that'd be too blas-
phemous, so you'll put yourself through the torture, and that will be your
pain, your price to pay for mankind. And it will be doubly painful,
because first they'll have to remove all the hair from your balls. But
that's good, since in the interim Nick Cave will no longer be confused
with the bearded wolf boy he's become in the 5 years since you added
him to your collection.

Who knows, maybe spilling piping hot coffee on your crotch might actually help remove that tattoo.

Your pal , Ernie B

4/14/99

Henry,

I know that it's you answering the 2.13.61 office phones, so you don't have to put up this ridiculous charade about claiming you're someone named Dave and that Henry's on tour somewhere doing spoken word. I've seen your schedule, I know you're at home. Sure, I was wrong about the Lamp Emporium mix-up, but how I was to know my phone was screwed up? Have you ever had a phone where the 2 and the 3 sounded exactly the same? Well if you have, you'll know why I got Lamp Emporium.

Did you know the 2.13 office's phone # is the first eleven notes of the Godfather theme (including the one and the area code)? It is. Try it. But then I don't know why you'd be calling the office when you're the guy answering the phones.

*Lance Crowder*

Lance Crowder


P.S. Any chance I could get my subscription to Rollins World re-instated? I already paid for a year and had only received one issue when I flew off the cuff and cancelled it. Thanks. Could I get all the back issues leading up to this month? At least could I get the issue where you're arm wrestling Sylvester Stallone on the cover in that celebrity arm wrestling event in Vegas? Or maybe start with the one where you're obedience training your dog.

April 15, 1999

Henry,

Jovan has relayed an interest in creating a perfume that would express-
ly fit your image, much like the Michael Jordan cologne currently on
the market. It would be a scent that encapsulates the essence of Henry
Rollins -- the olfactory essence of Henry Rollins -- in the best sense (no
pun intended). A tinge of sweat from your workout, or perhaps the
musky aroma of Henry after a spoken word show. They were even talking about adding a special pheromone, one that aromatically evokes the
specific desire you create onstage or through your recordings, and
caters to your specific demographic.

Possible names:

Whiff
Eau de l'Henry
Scent and Destroy
Smells Like Teen Rollins
Punk Significance
Rollinsurrection
Apprehension
Scent of Destruction

Before you say no, just think about how well Glenn Danzig did with
his Jovan offer.

Get back to me on this.

Keith Underwood
Underwood Management
(323) 77-POSER, FAX: (323) 777-2345

4-15-99

Dear Henry,

Sometimes when I pretend I'm you, I'll pretend I'm a horse
with deep psychological problems and you're a Horse
Whisperer, and we meet on this ranch in Montana because
the woman who owns me finds out through an article in
Western Horseman that you're the only person who can truly
help. At first you're reluctant to see me, because you've long
had mixed feelings about the state of Montana, the city of
Missoula in particular, but after much persistence on the part
of the woman who owns me you finally do come out to the
ranch. Immediately, you whisper sweet nothings into my ears
as you brush out my coat and mane, and feed me my oats
and clean the water in my trough. On the third day you invent
this special game called Pony Boy Express (even though I
hate ponies) where you ride me out to the main road to get
the mail everyday, and I whinny as you shout giddy-up, and
life is just so blissful. Deep down you want me to be yours
and eventually the woman who owns me says yes, that you
can keep me, but on the condition that you ride me bareback
always, which you agree to. And then we gallop off into the
sunset, our lives forever changed, so very happy that for the
rest of our days we can ride together free and unencum-
bered.

I'm not just dreaming, Henry. Roy Rogers didn't kiss his horse
at the end of each movie for nothing, you know.

Gerald Stubbins

# Hydrogen:
## It's Not Just for Breakfast Anymore

## NAM MYOHO RENGE KYO

*World peace through indestructible personal happiness*

Nichiren Shoshu of America
invites you to a question & answer meeting
to bring out your inherent wisdom and happiness
in order to reach your own unique potential

For information call: (555)333-2211

Chant with me Henry

NAM MYOHO RENGE KYO
NAM MYOHO RENGE KYO

— Carl Pluske

## -- Bill Mulholland Enterprises --

April 16, 1999

Dear Henry,

I just came across some letters on my computer that my brother Steve wrote to you, and I am faced with a bit of a dilemma. I don't know exactly how to say this, so let me put it to you in the form of a hypothetical:

For the past six months, piqued by a hung jury decision in which he allegedly used pepper spray to assault a co-worker, you've suspected that your brother is the loon-abomber, and it's tearing you up inside. You harbor deep sibling resentment because when you were a child, he ate some of your birthday cake before your party, then later that night cut your hair while you were sleeping and ran off with your father with money stolen from your mother's purse. The curious numbers he painted on your forehead took weeks to fade away, and your uncle has long suspected your brother had done some shoddy electrical work around his house. If you love your brother, is it worth trying to convince your uncle that the electrical shocks he's been getting are from squirrels chewing through the main cables in the central junction box?

Sincerely,

*Bill Mulholland*

Bill Mulholland

Subject: Sponges
Date:    04-16-99   08:05:19 EST
To:      HenryRollins@21361.com
From:    she@alisonhell.com (Alison Hell)

Henry, I can't remember the order of your sponges. Does it go
dishes/sink, kitchen counter, dogshit, linoleum floor? Or is it dish-
es/sink, dogshit, kitchen counter, and then the linoleum floor?

--Alison Hell

----------------------------------------

Subject: re: Sponges
Date:    04-17-99   19:06:13 EST
To:      she@alisonhell.com (Alison Hell)
From:    HenryRollins@21361.com

I told you last time, it's dishes, kitchen counter, kitchen sink,
bathroom sink, tub, then floors... I never said anything about
dogshit.

--Henry

Subj:    Mission Accomplished
Date:    04-17-99 22:58:23 EDT
To:      HenryRollins@21361.com
From:   JJ2341@floridacom.net

Henry Rolllns, you ROCK!! When I told everybody back here that you took us all to Disneyland, you shoulda seen their faces go all gangreen with envy (I shit you not).

So tell me, who was that Amy Svenske chick? How do you know her? Do you think she'd go out with me? She was hot. What if I shaved my safety haircut? That friend of hers Kimberly sure had a hard on for you. Dude, you're a regular Hugh Hefner!! Christ, if I'd a known that we were all going to get stuck on the Matterhorn for 5 hours until the emergency crews came and got us down one by one with that cherry picker, I woulda sat next to Amy Svenske instead of Speedo. I know everybody thought it was Speedo's fault that we got stuck, but they've had three hundred pound people on that ride before, so screw that. Sorry about all that vomit flying back into your face, the G's we were pulling on turn 4 were actually a lot stronger than anything I ever experienced at Great America, and I guess I wasn't ready for it. The good news is that after five hours, it was all dry, right?

So thanks again, Henry.

--Jimmy Jones

P.S. That sponge I used to wash your dishes when you weren't around? Well, just as we were leaving I noticed you cleaning the cat box with it so I guess it wasn't exactly the "dish" sponge.

April 20, 1999

Dear Mr. Rollins,

I wanted to thank you for showing my daughter Kimberly and her friend Amy around Los Angeles for the day. Please know that her father (my hot-head husband Duane who you met four years ago in that fracas on stage) and I pleaded with Kimberly not to bother you on her visit to California, emphasizing that the trip was for Amy Svenske, so she could see more than just North Carolina in her year here in the U.S. I honestly never thought they'd ditch their school tour group to search you out, but you know teenagers. Anyway, it was awfully sweet of you to take them both to Disneyland, paying their expenses and buying them Magic Kingdom t-shirts and sodas and stuffed animals, however unfortunate the events were that tran-spired later in Frontier Land at the Country Bear Jamboree. I thought that kind of unintentional Ed Ames hatchet-toss-groin-mishap only occurred on reruns of the Best of Carson. Yet despite your injury, you still managed to return the girls to their hotel that evening relatively unscathed.

Needless to say, I doubt the members of Ben Folds Five or Rage Against the Machine would have acted so gentlemanly in their roles as chaperon to two underage teenage girls.

Thank you again,

*Frances Evans*

Frances Evans
Raleigh, North Carolina

Subj:    Glomfort turnenbag
Date:    04-21-99 1:19:31 EDT
From:    Amysvenske@aol.com
To:      HenryRollins@21361.com


I lenrl,

It is partially with so very much fun that we visited you in
Disneyland California! Flying on the Magic Mountain of Frontier
merriment! It is for me the very best wave of the future days to
come. So now that I can return to my hinterland having confarted
with men and mice of all ages.

--Burlemt!      ---AmyS

To: Everyone at 2.13.61 (especially Rob Overton).

Now that Gus is living with Henry, it has become apparent that some of you need formal guidelines regarding your dealings with him. Please observe the following rules:

I promise to use discretion when playing with Gus.

I promise not to test Gus's limited amount of patience.

I promise not to place napkins on Gus's head for games of "Peasant Kitten."

I promise not to play "Kitten Rodeo," using Henry's red love beads.

I promise not to question Gus's inflated sense of self.

I promise not to stare at Gus when he is in the litter box.

I promise not to trick Gus with magic or games of probability.

I promise to stop sneaking Gus extra cans of cat food.

**GUS**
Lord of Napland and Ruling Emperor of Narco

You know what you need? You need to go on Oprah.
That'd boost those book sales. Man, just getting to
be a part of her Book Club would change everything. One day we'd turn the TV on and hear Oprah
say, "This week, Oprah Book Club Members, we're
going to be reading Henry Rollins' 'Solipsist' and a
fine book of tour journals entitled 'Get in the Van.'"
And you could give helpful reading hints, like "Make
sure you read Solipsist alone."

But what if you went on her show with a book
about relationships? That would slay. You could
write something like "First You Have to Love
Yourself" by Henry Rollins or maybe "Henry Rollins
Dating Tips for Troubled Teens." You'd be a natural.
Hell, I've seen you on "Loveline" with handy tips on
condom use (chewing gum in the receptacle tip?),
you would kill on Oprah. They'd fucking love you!
Just turn on that boyish Henry charm, so by the
time they bring out John Gray and his ex-wife to
duke it out over Mars and Venus, no one will give a
shit about those two, they'll only be interested in
you. Why stop at Venus and Mars when you can
shoot for the Stars?

But then everything would be different. The success
would most certainly go to your head. Within three
months you'll have pussed out and made the switch

to decaf and forgotten your core audience. Except you've already pussed out and made the switch to decaf, according to a guy I know who works at Starbucks on Melrose.

So maybe you should just stick to Jerry Springer. Go on his show and bust up some chairs. That would probably boost book sales too. Or at least t-shirt sales.

--Butch the Oreo King

P.S. Maybe this letter could be published in the next issue of Rollins World? I know you've been ignoring my requests but I've been reading the magazine at the newstand and the Letters section at the front is really lame. You need my letters, Rollins. C'mon, if I hadn't signed you up for that Haiku contest you would have never won.

YOU OWE ME, ROLLINS!!

5-5-99

Hey, I got the $200, the signed poster and
Black Flag vinyl, plus the subscription to
Rollins World magazine. Thanks!

But here's the catch: I'm not the guy who
advertised the Raffi bootlegs in Goldmine.
Hah! I don't even know what tapes you're
talking about! No kidding! I just happen to
have this guy Vince Atwater's old P.O. Box.
He's probably dead, for all I know, dead
from listening to all those children's
records. Do you know how many other Raffi
collectors I've strung along just like you?
I've lost count, to be honest. But it sure
has been fun yanking your chain, Rollins!
Are you familiar with the term mercy beat-
ing? Surely you've administered a few of
those in your day.

I think I've made my point.

Caveat Emptor

--Vince Atwater (?)

# Princeton University ⌛ Physics Department

May 30, 1999

Thompson--

We found him, but we'd probably better keep this under wraps. As far as anyone at 2.13.61 knows, he's only been missing for two weeks. It never occurred to us that he'd use the HDR Unit for such obvious historical tampering, so it wasn't until yesterday that Karen noticed the change in the original headline from the Tribune. Check for yourself, but this is how it now appears:

**New York Herald Tribune**
**April 16th, 1912**
**Titanic Sinks Despite Tattooed Mystery Man's Warning**

New York -- Numerous accounts among the Titanic's survivors refer to an unidentified mystery man appearing in the ship's Grand Ballroom on the fateful eve of April 14th to warn passengers and crew that the ship would be hitting an iceberg. The man, who refused to divulge his name, was placed in custody by Quartermaster George Rowe for the duration of the cruise, but most likely perished with the other 1500 passengers on board. When questioned about the man, Rowe replied "Yes, he appeared as if out of nowhere and was demanding to talk to Captain Smith. The ship's second officer, Charles Lightnoller, refused him, at which point this man began shouting in the Grand Ballroom that he was from the future and the ship was going to hit an iceberg and 1500 people were going to die. It took three of my men to restrain him, and when we brought him to the brig, we noticed a tattoo on his neck of four rectangles. We strip-searched him, whereupon we found a giant tattoo covering his back proclaiming 'Search and Destroy.' It was quite colorful, really, and I had never seen anything like it. Obviously a crazy man, though how he knew about the iceberg, well I'd have to venture it was just a lucky guess."

So this means that the Hyperdimensional Resonator is at the bottom somewhere with the  rest of the ship. Do we know if Ballard found anything in 1986 with the original dive? This could be a problem, especially if they did find it and are keeping it quiet. Christ, who knows what temporal repercussions Rollins has created this time.

--Edward Dyson

P.S. I just realized something: the "HDR" in Hyperdimensional Unit, those are Henry's initials. He'd appreciate the irony, I'm sure, wherever he is. Whenever he is.

# WANTED

## DEAD or ALIVE

# ROBERT K. OVERTON

# $25,000 REWARD

SIGNED: SHERIFF **Paul A. Schilling**

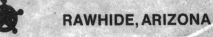

**RAWHIDE, ARIZONA**

May 30, 1999

Henry,

I probably should have told you I had an outstanding warrant for my arrest, right? "Outstanding!" is what I hope you'll say.

This doesn't mean you're going to fire me, though, right? I didn't exactly lie on my job application, I merely accented the positive, that's all.

You're not going to duct tape me into the trunk of your car and transport me across the state line to collect on the dough, are you? I don't think Paul Schilling is the Sheriff of Rawhide anymore, so you probably don't want to waste your time with the new Sheriff who's not familiar with my case. I'm pretty sure that when they get a new Sheriff, all the old Wanted posters come down off the wall to make room for the new. You know, to start fresh with a clean slate.

C'mon, I thought we were friends.

-- Rob O.

P.S. Where ya been? Everyone's been looking for ya.

I would like to thank the following people for helping with this book:

Henry Rollins, of course, and everyone at the 2.13.61 offices, including Carol Bua, Heidi May, Dave Belben (who looks nothing like his picture on "Dave's Page") and Elisa Jordan. Also Gary Hustwit and Jeff Aguila.

I'd also like to thank Gary Tieche, George Gary, Mary Clare Lingel, Duane Dell'Amico, and Larry Linsey, for their invaluable input, and several members of the Overton family, including Sandy, Rick, Carly Anne, and Teddy and Christian, for their help on the project, as well as Val Alderman and Gail "Guy!" Talbot. Also A.Ce and Daniella Diamond, Graydon Collins of Natural Energy in Snohomish, WA; Mom and Dad for their support, Nedley and Pamela Dahling, Bill and Terry Overton, Andre Burke, Woody "Willard" Neeley of the Connecticut Neeleys, Dave Rosshirt and Lorran, Maggie Furlong, Amy Lambert, Jeff Moreland, Hallie Prime, Marcus Crowder, Beth Winegarner, Patty Clark and Shea, and Emma the Girl Genius.

I would especially like to thank Alison Matochak without whom many of these letters would never have come to light. (Feel free to write Alison at her website at she@alisonhell.com-- she would love to hear from you!). The same special thanks goes to Bob Andrus, who although at the time of this writing is not yet on the Internet, was still able to function as the unwitting recipient of many of these letters in their early forms, snail mail or otherwise. Bob would also like to hear from you, and were it not for his Top Secret Level 5 U.S. Government MIB classification and undisclosed address, that would be entirely possible. But since people will probably write to him c/o 2.13.61 Publications anyway, please refrain from any questions about Bob's stint in Antarctica in the early 1980's as that is classified information also. However, if you have any questions about exotic birds or their Antarctic counterparts, he can provide information for a small fee. Please write to:

Exotic Bird Antarctic Counterparts
c/o Kirby's Bait and Seal Shop
Nome, Alaska     (zip code pending official postal reinstatement)

(Please do not write to us pointing out that Nome, Alaska is in inside the Arctic Circle, not the Antarctic Circle. We know this, as does Bob, who has been briefed on it many times).

And remember, keep writing to Henry, because not only does Henry love you, Henry loves to hear from you, too!

Henry Rollins, c/o 2.13.61 Publications, P.O. Box 1910, Los Angeles, CA 90078